Sexual Health

Independence
Educational Publishers
Cambridge

First published by Independence
PO Box 295
Cambridge CB1 3XP
England

British Library Cataloguing in Publication Data
Sexual Health – (Issues Series)
I. Donnellan, Craig II. Series
616.9'51

ISBN 1 86168 065 1

Printed in Great Britain
City Print Ltd
Milton Keynes

Typeset by
Claire Boyd

Cover
The illustration on the front cover is by
The Attic Publishing Co.

CONTENTS

Chapter One: HIV and AIDS

Chapter Two: Sexually Transmitted Diseases

Introduction

Sexual Health is the tenth volume in the series: **Issues**. The aim of this series is to offer up-to-date information about important issues in our world.

Sexual Health looks at the current situation regarding Aids, HIV and other sexually transmitted diseases.

The information comes from a wide variety of sources and includes:
Government reports and statistics
Newspaper reports and features
Magazine articles and surveys
Literature from lobby groups
and charitable organisations.

It is hoped that, as you read about the many aspects of the issues explored in this book, you will critically evaluate the information presented. It is important that you decide whether you are being presented with facts or opinions. Does the writer give a biased or an unbiased report? If an opinion is being expressed, do you agree with the writer?

Sexual Health offers a useful starting-point for those who need convenient access to information about the many issues involved. However, it is only a starting-point. At the back of the book is a list of organisations which you may want to contact for further information.

*****

Understanding HIV and AIDS

Information from the Terrence Higgins Trust

What are HIV and AIDS?

HIV is a virus which attacks the human immune system, the body's defence against disease. A person with HIV may feel completely well and have no symptoms.

In time, a person with HIV may develop particular rare illnesses or cancers because their immune system is weakened. When this happens, the person is said to have AIDS.

How does HIV cause AIDS?

HIV affects various parts of the body's immune system. The most important damage it causes is to certain white blood cells known as CD4 cells or T-helper cells. These cells are found in the lymph nodes as well as circulating round the body.

CD4 cells set other parts of the immune system in motion when organisms which cause disease are present in the body. These organisms include viruses, bacteria, protozoa and fungi. They can cause disease if not controlled by the immune system.

The CD4 cells of an HIV-infected person mount a defence against the invading HIV, and it may be held at bay for many years. But the virus is not completely destroyed, and it continues to attack the CD4 cells. Eventually the number of CD4 cells declines and the virus numbers rise.

When the CD4 cells start to decline, the person with HIV becomes vulnerable to other infections. The organisms which cause disease in people with HIV are common organisms, easily kept under control by the healthy immune system. They are able to cause illness only when the immune system is severely damaged, so the illnesses they cause are known as opportunistic infections.

Similarly, cells of the body go out of control all the time, and the immune system keeps them under control. If the immune system is damaged, these cells can cause opportunistic tumours.

Government centres for epidemiology[1] in the United States have compiled a list of serious illnesses and tumours which may result from immune system breakdown in a person with HIV. Once a person with HIV has experienced one or more of the conditions on this list, they are said to have AIDS.

HIV can also have direct effects upon the body. For example, the virus can attack cells in the brain and impair its working. One result of this is HIV encephalopathy (brain disease), and it is an AIDS-defining condition.

Recent research has shown that taking a combination of anti-HIV drugs (combination therapy) can slow down the effect of HIV on the immune system. When combination therapy is successful, it can improve and sustain the health of a person with HIV and will mean they are less likely to develop AIDS-defining conditions.

HIV in the UK

Since the start of the epidemic in the UK 30,001 people are known to have been infected with HIV.[2] 14,719 people have developed AIDS and 10,633 have died. During 1996, 2,896 new HIV infections were reported. This is the highest annual total ever and shows that the problem of HIV is not going away.

How do people become infected with HIV?

In order for a person to become infected, a sufficient amount of HIV must enter their bloodstream. This sufficient amount is the amount of HIV found in some, but not all, of the body fluids of someone with HIV or AIDS.

In a person with HIV or AIDS, the body fluids which contain enough HIV to infect someone else are:

- blood
- sperm and seminal fluid
- vaginal fluids, including menstrual fluids
- breast milk
- Other body fluids like saliva, sweat or urine do not contain enough virus to infect another person.

If HIV is present in body fluids, it still cannot enter another person's body easily. There are a limited number of routes:

- directly into the bloodstream; for example, via a puncture caused by injection equipment
- via an organ transplant or blood transfusion
- through the 'interior' skin (mucus membrane) of the rectum, vagina, cervix and urethra. The urethra is in front of the vagina in women and is the 'tube' in the penis in men
- very rarely, through the eyes, mouth or throat
- HIV cannot pass through intact external skin. It cannot pass through the air like cold germs.

See the Trust's booklet *Preventing HIV Infection* for information on preventing HIV transmission. See page 41 for address details.

HIV and sex

HIV can be passed from one person to another during penetrative sexual intercourse, that is, sex where the penis enters the vagina or anus.

Using a condom with water-based lubricant, or a femidom, during vaginal or anal penetrative sex will prevent transmission of HIV and many other sexually transmitted diseases.

HIV and sexual intercourse between men

Seven out of every 10 men with HIV in the UK were infected through sexual intercourse with another man. In the UK, northern Europe and parts of the United States, the most serious impact of the virus has been felt by the gay community. A large number of gay and bisexual men in the UK are still being infected every year: 1,474 tested HIV positive in 1995 and 1,634 in 1996.[3]

HIV and sexual intercourse between men and women

In the UK, fewer than 2 out of every 10 people with HIV were infected through sex with a member of the other sex who had HIV.

In 1995, 852 people were reported to have contracted HIV as a result of sexual intercourse with a person of the opposite sex who had HIV. In 1996 the number of people reported to have been infected in this way was 779.[3]

In Asia and sub-Saharan Africa HIV is transmitted most frequently by sexual intercourse between men and women. In the UK, HIV has had a devastating effect on communities of people from parts of Africa where HIV has taken hold.

HIV and oral sex

There have been about 20 cases world-wide where someone has become infected by giving oral sex to a man with HIV (sucking his penis). Where this has happened, it was probably because infected semen was able to pass through a cut or abrasion in the other partner's mouth or throat.

There are no confirmed reports of someone becoming infected

through giving oral sex to a woman with HIV (licking her labia or clitoris).

Someone whose genitals are sucked or licked by a person with HIV will not become infected, because saliva does not contain sufficient HIV to infect another person.

See the booklet by the Terrence Higgins Trust, *Oral Sex: a briefing for workers* for a detailed discussion of oral sex and HIV transmission. See page 41 for address details.

HIV and other sexual activities

One sexual activity which may be risky if one partner has HIV is sharing a sex toy: inserting an object into the vagina or anus of more than one person without washing it carefully between users or putting a clean condom on it between users.

HIV cannot be passed from one person to another through other sexual activities, including deep kissing, mutual masturbation, or via fingers inserted into the vagina or anus.

HIV and blood

HIV and shared injection equipment

One in ten (3,106 out of 30,101[2]) infections in the UK were acquired through sharing drug injecting equipment with someone with HIV. But sharing injecting equipment is not less risky than having sex with someone who has HIV. In Scotland, and in Southern Europe and parts of the United States, shared drug injecting equipment is the most common route of infection.

People who inject drugs can avoid transmitting HIV, either to themselves or to others, if they use a new set of injecting equipment every time or sterilise equipment between users. However, there is evidence that unsafe drug injecting is on the increase in this country.

HIV and blood transfusions

In the UK, 168 men and women were infected with HIV through transfusions of blood which contained the virus.

All blood donations and organ donations in the UK have been tested for HIV since 1985. The test may not be accurate if a person was very recently infected, and so people at risk of HIV are asked not to give blood.

In 1997, 3 people in the UK were discovered to be HIV positive through receiving blood donated by someone who had themselves been very recently infected with HIV. These cases are the only ones to have occurred in many millions of donations since 1985.

In some countries, infection through blood transfusion is still a significant risk.

Blood factor treatments

Factor 8 is a product of donated blood used in the treatment of haemophilia. Before it was known that donated blood might contain HIV, 1,196 men and boys with haemophilia became infected in the UK. Haemophilia is rare in women, and only 11 women were infected in this way. All Factor 8 is now heat treated, which kills HIV.

HIV and pregnancy

Mothers and babies

In the UK, the risk of HIV being transmitted from an HIV-infected woman to her baby before or during birth is about one in seven. In parts of the world where the standard of living and healthcare is not so high as here, the risk is greater.

HIV can also be passed to a baby during breastfeeding if the mother has HIV. In the UK, 423 babies born to women with HIV have had HIV themselves.

HIV and donated sperm

Just as a woman can be infected during sexual intercourse with a man who has HIV, she can also become infected through donated sperm if the donor has HIV.

Men who donate sperm to clinics are tested for HIV and their donations are guaranteed free from HIV.

What is an HIV test?

HIV is usually diagnosed by a blood test, known as an HIV antibody test or an HIV test. This test looks for antibodies formed by the immune system if HIV is present.

If HIV antibodies are found, the test is referred to as positive. The

UK HIV and AIDS update

Since the start of the epidemic in the UK 30,001 people are known to have been infected with HIV[2z] 14,719 people have developed AIDS and 10,633 have died.

Total cases of HIV, AIDS and AIDS deaths to end September 1997	
HIV	30,162
AIDS	14,719
AIDS deaths	10,663

AIDS cases and deaths for the last two 12-month periods:		
	10/95 - 9/96	10/96 - 9/97
AIDS cases	1,909	1,352
AIDS deaths	843	353

Source: National AIDS Trust

person is HIV antibody positive, often referred to as HIV-positive. If antibodies are not found, the test is negative and the person is HIV antibody negative or HIV-negative.

There is a gap, or 'window period', between infection and the formation of antibodies. This can last from a few weeks to three months. During this window period, the HIV antibody test will be negative even if HIV is present. That is why people who think they may have been infected need to wait for at least three months before they have a test. Some testing centres suggest a test after six months, to be absolutely sure.

HIV tests in the UK are highly accurate. A positive result is confirmed using a different technique. Negative tests are accurate so long as they are not done during the window period. Very occasionally the result may be unclear or 'equivocal'. When this happens a second test a few weeks later will give a clear result. See the booklet *Testing Issues* for further information about HIV tests.

Testing babies for HIV

Babies are born with their mothers' antibodies, which clear once the baby has developed its own immune system. Babies born to women with HIV have HIV antibodies in their blood from the mother for the first 18 months of life. An HIV antibody test on the baby's blood would show the mother's antibodies, and would

not tell the doctor whether the baby had HIV. Some hospitals are now able to perform tests on much younger babies of HIV-positive women, to discover whether the baby itself is infected with HIV.

What happens when someone has HIV?

Becoming HIV positive

Most people who become infected with HIV do not notice that they have been infected. A few weeks after infection, the body's immune system reacts to the virus by producing antibodies. Some people with HIV have a short 'seroconversion' illness at the time these antibodies are created.

The likely symptoms are the normal response to many other infections, and may include a sore throat, a fever or a rash.

Asymptomatic infection

The infected person may have no further outward signs or symptoms for many months or years. This is called asymptomatic infection.

Some people with asymptomatic infection have swollen lymph nodes, but this is not a sign of immune system damage. Nor are colds or flu: people with HIV do not get colds more often than other people. People who have HIV and feel completely well may have signs of immune damage detectable in laboratory tests on their blood.

Symptomatic infection

In time, immune damage may become more severe, though the increasing use of combination therapy may result in more people with HIV remaining well for longer. We do not know whether every person with HIV will eventually become ill.

Not all opportunistic infections are part of the AIDS definition, so a person with HIV may be quite ill but not have AIDS.

An AIDS diagnosis

AIDS itself does not have symptoms and there is no test for AIDS. The doctor will look for the specific illness causing the person's symptoms.

If they are caused by one of the AIDS-defining illnesses, and if the patient has HIV, then he or she is said to have AIDS.

Examples of illnesses which will result in an AIDS diagnosis, if HIV is present:

- pneumocistis carinii pneumonia (PCP), a rare form of pneumonia common in people with HIV
- cytomegalovirus (CMV), a member of the herpes family which can cause blindness and serious gastrointestinal, brain and lung problems in people with HIV

Someone with AIDS is likely to enjoy periods of comparatively good health between bouts of serious illness. Some people have lived for several years with an AIDS diagnosis.

People taking combination therapy successfully will be less likely to develop AIDS-defining illnesses.

Treatments for HIV and AIDS

Increasingly, it is possible to prevent or treat opportunistic infections using new drugs. For example, PCP was a frequent cause of death in people with AIDS in the early years of the epidemic. Doctors are now able to prevent PCP with drugs, or to treat it quickly if it occurs. Death from PCP is now rare among people with HIV in the UK.

Research studies show that the most effective way to attack HIV is with a combination of anti-HIV drugs. Combination therapy is a huge advance in the treatment of HIV, and many people have done very well on it.

Combination therapy is not easy to take (the various drugs have to be taken at different times according to a strict timetable), and there are side effects. It does not work for everyone, and where it does work we do not know how long that will last. Sometimes the drugs stop working because people develop resistance to them.

Research is continuing all the time to make combination therapies more effective and easier to take.

Some people with HIV and AIDS use complementary treatments to help with their symptoms. Examples are acupuncture, aromatherapy and homeopathy.

There is no vaccine or cure available yet, but scientists' understanding of how the virus works continues to improve. However, drug treatments and vaccines are expensive to develop, and it is not likely that people in some countries will be able to benefit from new discoveries for the foreseeable future.

Living with HIV

Even though there are now more effective anti-HIV treatments, living with the knowledge of a serious and potentially life-threatening infection is likely to be stressful and difficult. Someone with HIV may remain in

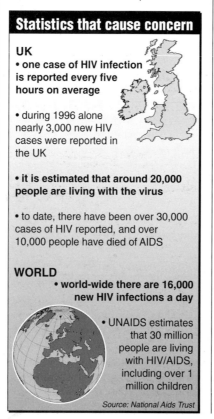

Statistics that cause concern

UK
- **one case of HIV infection is reported every five hours on average**
- during 1996 alone nearly 3,000 new HIV cases were reported in the UK
- **it is estimated that around 20,000 people are living with the virus**
- to date, there have been over 30,000 cases of HIV reported, and over 10,000 people have died of AIDS

WORLD
- **world-wide there are 16,000 new HIV infections a day**
- UNAIDS estimates that 30 million people are living with HIV/AIDS, including over 1 million children

Source: National Aids Trust

good physical health for several years but misunderstanding and fear about HIV and AIDS is still widespread in society. People living with the virus may encounter hostility or rejection even from friends and family and some people have lost jobs and homes due to their employers' or landlords' attitudes, and children with HIV have been banned from schools.

Many people with HIV have seen friends and partners become ill before them, and may have seen friends die. Some communities have been more affected by HIV than others: for example, gay men, people from sub-Saharan African communities and injecting drug-users. In some parts of the world, and among African families in the UK, it is not unusual for whole families to die with AIDS.

Many people with HIV choose to tell no one about their diagnosis except for a few trusted friends, and this burden of secrecy can be very hard to bear. Living with the knowledge that you could pass a serious infection to someone else can also be very hard. A number of support groups have been set up round the country to help counter the isolation which HIV can cause.

Many people with HIV make changes in their lives to help them cope with their diagnosis. Some choose to work at keeping fit and healthy with good food and exercise; others may read up about HIV and become their own experts in drug treatments or complementary therapies. Some people with HIV have said that focusing on living and enjoying life to the full has helped them to cope with living with HIV.

References
1 Epidemiology is the study of how diseases affect populations of people.
2 Public Health Laboratory Service *CDR Weekly Communicable Diseases Report*, Vol 7, no 43, 24 October 1997. Statistics to the end of September 1997.
3 Public Health Laboratory Service *CDR Weekly Communicable Diseases Report*, Vol 7, no 4, 24 January 1997. Statistics to the end of December 1996.

Sexual diseases epidemic getting worse as Aids claims 10,000

By Jeremy Laurance,
Health Editor

The worst epidemic of modern times has failed to alter the nation's sexual habits which are continuing to put the health of young people at risk.

Aids has claimed the lives of over 10,000 people in Britain but years of warnings about the dangers of casual and unprotected sex have gone unheeded. Sexually transmitted diseases, including Aids, are rising and there is no chance that target reductions set under the Government's Health of the Nation strategy will be achieved. Professor Michael Adler, of University College Hospital, London, Britain's leading Aids specialist, says blame for the failure must in part be laid on the last Government's agenda of family values and morality. Professor Adler, who is married to Baroness Jay, the Labour health minister, says attempts to withhold information about sex from young people 'have resulted in large numbers not protecting themselves against sexually transmitted diseases and unwanted pregnancy'.

Latest figures, published in the *British Medical Journal*, show the commonest sexually transmitted diseases – chlamydia and genital warts – are increasing. There is an inner-city epidemic of gonorrhoea, linked to poverty and mainly affecting gay men and people from

> **Cases of Aids and HIV reached their highest totals in 1996 with almost 2,986 newly reported infections and 1,862 people with the full-blown disease**

ethnic groups. Professor Adler says: 'The incidence of sexually transmitted diseases as a whole has not declined and has even increased slightly.'

Teenage conceptions rose in 1994, after falling between 1989 and 1993, and now stand at 8.4 per 1000 girls under 16 compared with the Health of the Nation target of 4.8 by 2000.

Cases of Aids and HIV reached their highest totals in 1996 with almost 2,986 newly reported infections and 1,862 people with the full-blown disease. Homosexuals in particular appear to be eschewing safe sex. The number of infections acquired through sex between men rose 11 per cent between 1995 and 1996.

However, anonymous testing of blood from pregnant women and from patients at sexually transmitted disease clinics shows HIV infection is also rising among heterosexuals.

© The Independent
June, 1997

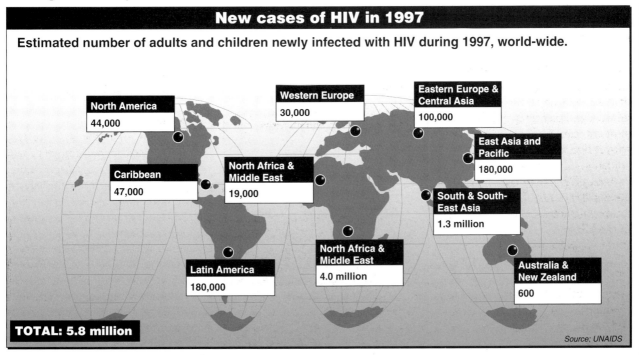

New cases of HIV in 1997

Estimated number of adults and children newly infected with HIV during 1997, world-wide.

North America
44,000

Western Europe
30,000

Eastern Europe & Central Asia
100,000

East Asia and Pacific
180,000

Caribbean
47,000

North Africa & Middle East
19,000

South & South-East Asia
1.3 million

Latin America
180,000

North Africa & Middle East
4.0 million

Australia & New Zealand
600

TOTAL: 5.8 million

Source: UNAIDS

Aids 2000

By the end of the millennium, the focus of the worst of the Aids pandemic will have shifted from Africa to South East Asia and the former Soviet Union. A vaccine to halt the spread of HIV may still be an elusive hope, and the escalating cost of treatments for people with Aids will threaten the economies of countries world-wide. Keith Alcorn reports

Who will be worst hit?

South East Asia and the former Soviet Union will bear the brunt of Aids in the 21st century as the focus of the Aids epidemic switches away from Africa.

Patterns of infection in the former Soviet Union now mirror those seen in the early years of epidemics in Thailand and North America. HIV prevalence amongst injecting drug users in one Black Sea port, Niklayev, rose from 1.7 per cent in January 1995 to 56.5 per cent by the end of 1995. Injecting drug use is now extremely widespread in Russia, Ukraine and Belarus, and in early 1996 it was estimated that 10,000 people were already infected in Ukraine alone.

Rates of sexually transmitted infections in Russia should also serve as a warning that the country is set to experience a Thai-style epidemic of HIV infection quite unlike anything seen in Western Europe. 325,000 cases of syphilis were reported in 1996 in Russia, a rate 100 times higher than Western Europe, and earlier this year the UK's public health laboratory reported that one in five syphilis diagnoses in the UK between 1994 and 1996 were linked to travel in Russia or Eastern Europe. But what makes the Russian epidemic especially disturbing is the government response to the disease. While most African and South East Asian countries have respected the human rights of HIV-infected people, Russia now has the most draconian laws anywhere in the world. Russian Aids activists say that the government is repeating all the worst aspects of the Soviet regime by establishing what amounts to an 'Aids gulag', a concentration camp for HIV-positive criminals in the Arctic Circle province of Pechora.

HIV testing has also become compulsory for Russians returning from travel abroad and for anyone attending sexually transmitted disease clinics. Post-test counselling often consists of the presentation of a document advising that 'you are the carrier of a deadly disease and are criminally liable for any contact that would pass that disease to another person'. However, injecting drug use remains the main route of transmission of HIV, and local opium derivatives cooked up on kitchen stoves have been responsible for several massive outbreaks of infection in towns throughout Russia this year. As in the United States, needle exchange is not a politically acceptable option, says Oscar Bernal of Médecins Sans Frontières, an international relief agency working in Russia.

In South East Asia, UN Aids Programme Director Peter Piot says that infections are set to double between now and 2000, to 14 million, with the largest numbers in India, Vietnam and China. One in 100 people in India and Vietnam could be HIV-positive by 2000 unless more is done to promote condom use and bring injecting drug use under control. Other countries which have seen massive escalations in HIV infections over the past two years are

---

Patterns of infection in the former Soviet Union now mirror those seen in the early years of epidemics in Thailand and North America

---

Nigeria and South Africa; it is estimated that nearly two million of Nigeria's 100 million inhabitants will be infected by 2000, whilst nearly three and a half million are already estimated to be infected in South Africa out of a population of less than 25 million.

What hope for a vaccine for HIV?

However much excitement may have been generated by advances in HIV treatment over the past few years, the impact of these improvements will represent a mere drop in the ocean unless an effective vaccine against HIV can be developed soon.

Widespread controversy has greeted a proposal by Dr Charles Farthing and the International Association of Physicians in Aids Care to begin tests of a live Aids vaccine on volunteer physicians in the US and Europe. The proposal is controversial because many experts believe that a live Aids vaccine is unsafe, and that it will lead to illness and death in a significant proportion of those vaccinated, just as it has in monkeys. Even if such trials never go ahead (which looks more and more likely as labs around the world report increasingly gloomy news about primates given weakened but still live forms of SIV, the primate equivalent of HIV), the controversy has rekindled international debate about the need for a vaccine, and the desperate shortage of promising candidates. Although it is unrealistic to expect that the first generation of HIV vaccines will provide 100 per cent protection to 100 per cent of those vaccinated, finding a vaccine which is even 50 per cent effective raises a host of difficult logistical and ethical issues, not least, who will pay for it and who will it be tested on?

Julian Meldrum of the National Aids Trust is a member of the International Aids Vaccine Initiative, a lobby group trying to move vaccine research forward. Like Dr Charles Farthing, he believes that people in Europe and North America must expect to take part in such trials, and shouldn't assume that all the risk will be carried by people in Africa and Asia. But whilst Dr Farthing is proposing a safety trial amongst physicians (on the grounds that doctors have always exposed themselves to risk in order to cure disease), Julian Meldrum argues that 'a vaccine will need to be tested amongst all high-risk groups to determine whether it protects against exposure through blood, through the vagina and through the rectum. Different sub-types of HIV appear to have adapted better to some transmission routes than others.'

Preventing the global spread of HIV requires two things apart from a vaccine, one probably more feasible than the other. One is a vaginal microbicide, a chemical which can be used by women during sex to kill HIV. The other is a huge reduction in the supply of heroin and the use of injectable drugs. But underlying these requirements, say prevention experts, are much greater changes in the structure of societies and the global distribution of wealth. The vulnerability of women and the global trade in heroin are just symptoms.

However, a microbicide could be closer than a vaccine, and at last year's International Aids Conference experts agreed that a prevention method which could be controlled by women rather than men would have a significant impact on infection rates in developing countries. Several products are now entering large-scale clinical trials, but even if an effective, convenient and safe microbicide is developed in the next few years, it is unclear how women in developing countries will be able to afford to use it.

Paying to stop Aids

The developing world cannot afford to fight Aids, yet it cannot afford not to. This is the message which has become abundantly clear as more

and more countries pass through the four stages of the epidemic. The first stage is 'invisible spread', a period usually accompanied by official denial of the existence of widespread high risk behaviour in a society. China is a good example of a country which has only recently emerged from this stage. The second phase is 'early stigmatisation', and invariably involves the isolation and rejection of people in marginalised groups who are beginning to develop Aids. Sex workers in Myanmar, injecting drug users in Russia and gay men in the West have all been stigmatised. At this point there is little investment in the clean needles and condoms which might have a huge impact on future infection rates.

The developing world cannot afford to fight Aids

The third phase is 'mass behaviour change', which involves an admission that HIV is spreading outside stigmatised groups. India, Thailand and South Africa have reached this stage, but only Thailand has yet mounted an effective national campaign to encourage condom use. The fourth phase is 'economic impact', which characterises the epidemics now being experienced in Africa, the USA and Western Europe. This is the point at which treatment costs begin to outweigh those of prevention, and when illness and death begin to have a wider effect on the economy, as in Botswana, Uganda and Zimbabwe.

Some nations are paying especially heavily for earlier failure

to control HIV, with spiralling drug budgets or overcrowded hospitals. In Europe, Spain and Italy are worst affected, with more than 150,000 HIV-infected people in each country already requiring treatment. This phenomenal financial burden will place a massive strain on public services, and it's one of the time-bombs under European Monetary Union as states struggle to cut public spending in order to meet the convergence criteria for the single currency.

In Asia the cost to the so-called Tiger Economies could be just as great as the recent stock-market crash. The cost of Aids in lost output for Cambodia alone could be $2.8 billion by 2000, according to Peter Piot of UN Aids, with correspondingly higher costs in neighbouring countries. Recent advances in treatment are unlikely to be affordable throughout the developing world. Thai health economists estimated that to provide everyone infected with dual combination therapy would increase the Thai Aids budget by 630 per cent, whilst the task of identifying HIV-positive mothers during pregnancy and giving AZT to prevent mother-to-baby transmission would mean a budget increase of just 16 per cent. Unsurprisingly the Thai government chose the cheaper option.

Whilst some advocates in the West argue that pharmaceutical companies and governments have a duty to provide drugs at greatly subsidised rates, some experts don't believe that it is that simple. 'The infrastructure to provide anti-retroviral therapy effectively doesn't even exist in most developing countries,' says Professor Kevin de Cock of the London School of Tropical Medicine, who has worked extensively in Africa. And if Western governments and companies are going to engage in a massive handout of drugs, why should they do it for HIV rather than tuberculosis, which kills far more people and is easier to treat?

An international relief effort will probably need to combine the treatment of HIV and TB if it is to win support from donors such as the World Bank.

New developments in treatment

By the millennium it's likely that the face of Aids treatment will have changed just as much as it has over the last three years, due to the arrival of several new types of anti-HIV drugs.

First among these are the fusion inhibitors, which stop HIV getting into T-cells. Also on the horizon are bicyclams and integrase inhibitors, as well as protease inhibitors which work in a different way to the ones currently being marketed.

Also on the horizon are the nucleotide analogues and new versions of the types of drugs which are already in use – nucleoside analogues, protease inhibitors and non-nucleoside reverse transcriptase inhibitors. If these drugs reach the market they will provide a further option beyond the 12 drugs currently available to treat HIV infection. Although this may sound like a lot of drugs, thousands of people in Europe and the USA have already exhausted the available options just 18 months after the arrival of the protease inhibitors. For them, new drugs are an urgent necessity. Unfortunately it's certain that many of these candidates will fall by the wayside long before they get a licence. This may be because they don't work, but it could also be because companies which currently hold the patents have no idea how to develop the drugs.

HIV therapy could also become easier to take. Much interest currently focuses on new delivery systems for anti-HIV drugs.

One of the problems inherent in the way that protease inhibitors work is the speed with which the drugs are cleared from the bloodstream. This means that the drugs have to be taken frequently and regularly to avoid the development of resistance – three times a day in some cases. Significant numbers of people have problems adhering to such rigid and onerous schedules, with the result that the treatments fail for large numbers of people.

Pharmacologists are looking at a number of systems, including slow-

The Communicable Disease Surveillance Centre estimates that in the UK around 1,000 gay men are being infected with HIV each year even now

release tablets and transdermal patches similar to those already used to deliver nicotine. Injections are another possibility, but this is only likely to work if the number of active drugs in a regimen can be reduced, since having to have injections on top of pills is unlikely to work in favour of better compliance.

Companies are also looking at reducing doses by putting drugs together in the same capsule. The first multi-drug capsule is likely to reach the pharmacy in 1998, when Glaxo-Wellcome will launch its Combivir capsule, combining doses of AZT and 3TC in one capsule.

The commercial logic of such a development is indisputable, and other such moves can be expected as the portfolio of HIV drugs is increasingly concentrated in the hands of a few major players. Although dozens of companies are involved in researching and developing anti-HIV drugs, only a few companies probably have the know-how and the muscle to successfully exploit these products in the market place.

Things that will not have changed by 2000

One thing that will not have changed by 2000 is the need for condom use. There's no evidence that current therapies can achieve a cure, and there is an increasing consensus that therapy will have to be lifelong. Preventing new infections amongst gay men will continue to be a priority, despite cuts in funding for HIV prevention.

On the basis of its anonymised HIV testing and other calculations, the Communicable Disease Surveillance Centre estimates that in the UK around 1,000 gay men are being infected with HIV each year even now. Whilst this infection rate is considerably lower than the US, and much lower than during the early 1980s, it represents the potential for 10,000 new infections over the next decade, overwhelmingly in London. If European trends are followed over here, between 15 and 30 per cent could be infected with drug-resistant viruses which severely limit the men's treatment options.

Another thing that won't change between now and 2000 is the gradual withdrawal of Government money from the voluntary sector, support services and HIV prevention outside London. Whilst the Government has granted an extra £23 million to HIV treatment next year (one of the few areas of public spending to grow in 1998), this will not cover the growth in HIV drug budgets, so health authorities will have to cut money from elsewhere to cover drug costs.

In London voluntary organisations are being encouraged to consider mergers and a streamlining of services, and it's quite possible that by 2000 the needs of people with HIV will be met by a smaller spectrum of HIV organisations. Whether this means a decline in the range of services offered will depend in part on what happens to people currently benefiting from the new treatments. If they continue to benefit, this will reduce long-term demand for welfare and care services. But if they cease to benefit, many HIV organisations could find themselves increasingly hard pressed.

• Keith Alcorn is editor of *The Aids Reference Manual* published by National Aids Manual Publications.

© Aids 2000

Young people at risk

Information from UNAIDS

In some parts of the world, the proportion of the total adult population living with HIV/AIDS has stabilised or begun to fall. While this is good news, it can hide an unpleasant truth: new infections in the younger age groups can continue unabated or even go on rising as the overall proportion of people living with HIV/AIDS falls.

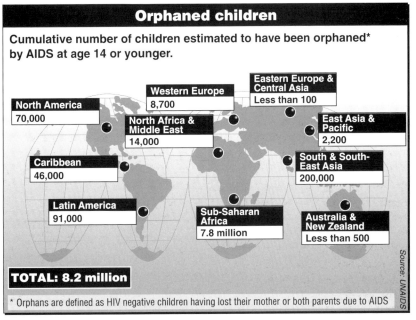

Orphaned children

Cumulative number of children estimated to have been orphaned* by AIDS at age 14 or younger.

North America
70,000

Western Europe
8,700

Eastern Europe & Central Asia
Less than 100

North Africa & Middle East
14,000

East Asia & Pacific
2,200

Caribbean
46,000

South & South-East Asia
200,000

Latin America
91,000

Sub-Saharan Africa
7.8 million

Australia & New Zealand
Less than 500

TOTAL: 8.2 million

Source: UNAIDS

* Orphans are defined as HIV negative children having lost their mother or both parents due to AIDS

High infection rates and risk behaviour among some young people

In most parts of the world, the majority of new infections are in young people between the ages of 15 and 24, sometimes younger. In one study in Zambia, over 12% of the 15 and 16-year-olds seen at antenatal clinics were already infected with HIV.

Girls appear to be especially vulnerable to infection, but Uganda has recently shown encouraging evidence that in some city sites infection rates have halved among teenage girls since 1990. Even there, however, the rates remain unacceptably high, with up to 1 pregnant teenager in 10 testing HIV-positive. That rate is six times higher than in boys of the same age.

In South Africa, the proportion of pregnant 15/19-year-olds infected with HIV rose to 13% in 1996 from around half that level just two years earlier. In Botswana the infection rate stood at 28% for the same group in 1997. In Maharashtra state in India, where the epidemic is in its early years, some 3.5% of pregnant teenagers tested HIV-positive in a recent study.

What is abundantly clear is that some young people all over the world engage in risky sexual behaviour. In Mongolia, there has been a recent jump in sexually transmitted diseases in children under 15, indicating that they are exposed to unprotected intercourse. One study shows that since 1994, STDs in those under 15 have shot up more than tenfold. In Namibia, 37% of 12/18-year-olds reported that they had had sex, nearly half of them with more than one partner. Most said that they believed their own partners had had other partners, too. In Tanzania, 12% of teenage males and 37% of 20/24-year-olds reported that they had multiple sex partners in the last year. In Mali, 2 out of 5 sexually active boys in their teens said they last had sex with a prostitute or casual partner. In the United States, some studies indicate that genital herpes has jumped more than fourfold among white teenagers since the 1970s, with close to 1 in 20 now infected. Among white Americans in their 20s, the rate is 1 in 7.

Sometimes, young people know of the risks of unprotected sex but feel AIDS could not possibly happen to them. In Malawi, most young men and women know how HIV is transmitted and how it can be

In most parts of the world, the majority of new infections are in young people between the ages of 15 and 24

prevented. When asked, however, many said they felt invulnerable to the virus. Some 90% of teenage boys said they were at no risk or at minimal risk of infection, even though nearly half of them reported at least one casual sex partner over the last year, and condom use was low.

Even in countries such as Thailand – which has been among the most successful in encouraging young people to adopt safer sexual behaviour and has been rewarded by seeing a marked fall in both HIV infection and other STDs – there are groups of young people that fall through the net, such as those living on the street.

More education translates into lower risk

In many countries, young people are denied access to education about HIV including safe behaviour skills, or are unable to buy condoms or attend STD clinics. This is usually because older adults believe such education and services will actually encourage young people to increase their sexual activity.

In fact, the reverse is true according to a newly-published UNAIDS review of data from four continents. Good-quality sex education helps delay first intercourse and leads to lower levels of teenage pregnancy and STDs. In the years after Switzerland launched an active and very open campaign aimed at informing young people about healthy sexual behaviour, the proportion of 17-year-old girls and boys who never had sex – a proportion that had been dropping for many years – began to show a marked rise. The same trend toward postponement of first sexual intercourse is now being observed in the USA and in Uganda.

Educational efforts are also resulting in greater condom use among those who have become sexually active. Thailand and Uganda have already been mentioned. In Tanzania, 16% of sexually active teenage women had used a condom in 1996. While this may seem woefully low, it is certainly a vast improvement on the 5% recorded in 1990. The proportion of teenage boys who had ever used a condom rose from 14% to 38% in the same period. In Zambia, too, condom use has risen from very low

levels in the 1980s. In 1996 about one-third of sexually active teenage girls nation-wide reported having used a condom – a level previously reported only from the capital Lusaka, where condom use has always been highest. In Switzerland, levels of casual sex among young people have remained more or less constant since the late 1980s, but consistent use of condoms with those partners has risen fourfold – a more impressive increase than seen in older people.

© UNAIDS

Tragedy on an epic scale

More than eight million children have lost one or both parents to Aids. Ian Hunt assesses the impact of HIV, and examines the role of sex education in preventing the spread of this deadly virus

This year World Aids Day has focused attention on the effects of Aids (Acquired Immune Deficiency Syndrome) on children. Many more people are affected than are infected. The death of a parent or both parents is devastating for a child, and over 8 million children around the world have now become orphans as a result of Aids.

In poor and developing countries, where the effect of Aids is much worse, the oldest children who become orphans may have little time or opportunity to get over their loss. They will probably have to become the wage-earner and carer for younger brothers and sisters. Aunts, uncles, and grandparents may help, but there is a limit to what families can do. Maintaining hope in these circumstances is hard, but children do find ways of carrying on: even in places where prejudice and ignorance remain.

Children themselves are at risk of infection. In the developing world approximately 25-35 per cent of children born to mothers who carry HIV, the virus that causes Aids, will also carry the virus, either at birth or through breastfeeding. In the richer countries the rate is 12-15 per cent.

Children's bodies are more vulnerable to infection; they are less

able to live with the virus than adults, and are more likely to die of diseases they catch as a result. HIV, or Human Immunodeficiency Virus, attacks the body's immune system, the means by which it resists disease.

Children are also liable to infection because they are becoming young people and adults. At this crucial stage they should not be denied information about the ways the virus can be transmitted through unprotected sex, or feel that they are unable to talk to anyone about their

concerns. Sixty per cent of new infections world-wide are among young people of 16 to 24.

Sex education

At whatever age young people become sexually active, which varies greatly from person to person, they need to have people they can talk to who will give them good advice and information. This is sometimes difficult for parents and guardians to accept: some seem to forget rather quickly what being young was like.

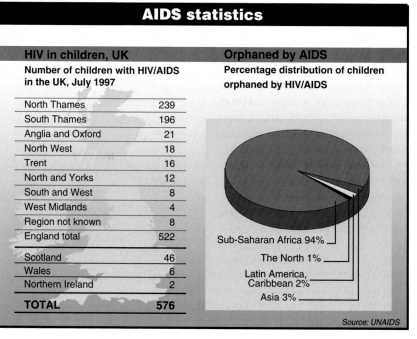

AIDS statistics

HIV in children, UK

Number of children with HIV/AIDS in the UK, July 1997

North Thames	239
South Thames	196
Anglia and Oxford	21
North West	18
Trent	16
North and Yorks	12
South and West	8
West Midlands	4
Region not known	8
England total	522
Scotland	46
Wales	6
Northern Ireland	2
TOTAL	**576**

Orphaned by AIDS

Percentage distribution of children orphaned by HIV/AIDS

Sub-Saharan Africa 94%
The North 1%
Latin America, Caribbean 2%
Asia 3%

Source: UNAIDS

Not everyone wants to talk to their parents about sex, and not all parents can answer their questions or appreciate their concerns. Confidentiality may be essential if you are gay or bisexual, as it is not always easy to know how people will react.

Talking about sex does not necessarily encourage people to become sexually active younger. In Holland young Netherlanders, who receive a coherent programme of sex education, report having heterosexual intercourse at an average age of 17.5 years; in the UK the average age is about 16. In Holland, the teenage conception rate is one-seventh that of England and Wales.

Information about HIV and sexually transmitted diseases needs to be conveyed in stages, as part of a coordinated plan. Many diseases are quite common, and most are easily treated, and it is vitally important for your health that they are treated. But no one should pretend that sex is just a question of biology and disease.

Sex education should give enough space to people's need to find ways to talk about sex and its complex place in life. Sex is a communication and a negotiation of another's feelings and wishes. It involves the power of attraction, but in the early stages it also involves the power of what your friends say, which strongly influences your sense of what 'normal' sexuality is. That subtle influence on you from your friends can be hard to talk about, too.

The most successful education campaigns around the world recognise and turn to advantage the powerful influence on our behaviour of our friends and contemporaries. By training school-leavers and young people as educators and advice workers, information is conveyed much more effectively. The young sexual health education activists also talk to families and so the needs of adults are met to some extent.

The difficulties surrounding HIV, such as the stigma which HIV-carriers may suffer, can be hard to confront. And because the main route of HIV transmission world-wide is from a man to a woman, the relative power of men and women must be considered.

People often make the mistake of thinking that not to use a condom is to trust a person more, when, in fact, to insist on safe sex is to care more for someone else, whether as part of a long-term relationship or as an experimental fling.

Sexually transmitted infections

HIV is one of a number of sexually transmitted infections (STIs). Some of the most common are gonorrhoea, chlamydia and genital warts. Some STIs have been on the increase in the UK. This is worrying news, because the link between STIs and the incidence and susceptibility to HIV infection is well known.

The global fight against Aids is a battle against other sexually transmitted diseases, too. 30.6 million people carry HIV, but it has been estimated that there are 333 million cases of STIs globally, nearly half of which are believed to be in south-east Asia. Treatment of STIs reduces the risk of HIV.

Questions people ask

What counts as safe sex?
Mutual masturbation (manual stimulation), sexual intercourse using a condom, kissing, stroking, caressing. And talking together about what feels good.

What are the risks of HIV transmission through oral sex?
Disputed, but very small; real when stimulating an HIV positive man if you have sores or cuts around your mouth. Almost all sexual transmission of HIV is through intercourse without a condom.

In what other ways can HIV be spread?
It can get into another person's blood when needles are shared between injecting drug users. And it can be transmitted from mother to baby at birth or through breastfeeding when the mother is HIV positive. Blood transfusions of infected blood have also given people HIV in the past, but all blood is now screened.

Chlamydia
This condition is easily treated but is on the increase (39,000 reported cases in genito-urinary clinics in 1995). The symptoms are bleeding or discharge, or pain when urinating. But up to 90 per cent of men and 25 per cent of women with chlamydia have no symptoms. As with most STIs, chlamydia can lead to other infections if left untreated (around 65,000 'non-specific genital infections' were reported in 1995) in both men and women.

Thrush (Candidiasis)
Not necessarily sexually transmitted. Thrush in women produces itching and vaginal discharge, and swelling of the vulva; in men, soreness or inflammation of the penis. Treated with anti-fungal cream or pessaries. Live yoghurt can also work against the yeast responsible for thrush.

Genital herpes
27,000 cases in 1995, most common among 20-24-year-olds. Tingling or itching in the genital area, followed by small painful blisters (the sexually infectious stage); flu-like symptoms. There's no cure but drugs are available to reduce the severity of the first attack, after which most people will recover.

Gonorrhoea
Treated with antibiotics. 12,000 cases reported in 1995, and on the increase again, particularly amongst women aged 16-19, and men aged 20-24. Symptoms differ for men and women; most women do not have any symptoms. Men experience a discharge from the penis and a burning pain when urinating. Gonorrhoea passed on through oral sex does not usually cause symptoms. As with all STIs, anal gonorrhoea in gay men must be treated.

Genital warts
The most common sexually transmitted infection: 93,000 reported cases in 1995. And again it is young people who are most likely to catch the virus that causes the warts, which develop around the genitals and anus, and may be just inside the body. They are painless, and resemble other warts, but need to be treated in men

and in women, where there is a proven link with the development of cervical cancer.

A family's experience of the illness

Jenny Driscoll of Actionaid talked to 17-year-old Takondwa Chidzankufa in her village in Malawi

Can you tell me what happened when your mum first told you that she was HIV positive?

When she told us, me and my sister, that she was HIV positive we were all worried and my sister started crying. She said we should just pray for her so that she would have a long life and encourage her and help her, when she would be sick.

How do you help your mum?

I make her bed and I cook for her. I remind her when it's time to take her drugs. So she takes them at the right time.

What about your friends. Do you tell them that your mum is HIV positive?

At first I didn't tell them. Now at school we have an Aids club where we discuss Aids, the way to prevent it and how to help those who are HIV positive. One day I decided to tell my friends that my mum was HIV positive.

What did your mum tell you about HIV/Aids?

My mum told us the way HIV is transmitted and she advised us to take care of ourselves and not to point fingers at those who are HIV positive, because you don't know what could come next. And that we should pray for her . . . and teach our friends about HIV/Aids.

What do you say to your friends about HIV/Aids?

Most of the time when I'm chatting with my friends at school I like to warn them about Aids, just because I know the problems which are brought with Aids because I have experienced them. So I always tell them to be careful.

And what are the problems which come with HIV/Aids?

Well, at our home there is little care since my mum uses the money to buy medicine. And to take care of us she tries her best so that she should share with us the best she can while she's alive.

And what do you want to do when you leave school?

When I grow up I'd like to be a journalist.

And what will you write about?

I would write about Aids and the many stories I have experienced about it. And the many things I have experienced in life.

What is life like now that your mum is HIV positive?

At first my life was a happy life. Now when I look at my mum sometimes she looks worried and, when she's sick, most of the times I can see she is thinking I might die today and who will look after my children? Sometimes she is very quiet but I encourage her not to be worried. Mostly, I spend time chatting with her when we are free.

Do you look after your sister?

Yes, and I teach her how to look after mum when I'm away.

Further information

- An activity pack for schools on HIV/Aids is available from Actionaid, price £2. Further information on education work with young people around the world from Actionaid, Chataway House, Leach Rd, Chard, Somerset TA20 1FA (01460-62972) and from Save the Children Fund, 17 Grove Lane, London SE5 8RD (0171-703 5400).

- The Terrence Higgins Trust, 52-54 Gray's Inn Road, London WC1X 8JU http://www.tht.org.uk. Advice and information for those with HIV and Aids.

- Material supporting the theme of World Aids Day, *Children Living in a World with Aids*, has been published online by Avert, the education and research trust, at http://www.avert.org. See also Actionaid's website, http://www.actionaid.org. Actionaid

- Thousands of people in the UK are catching sexually infectious diseases. It is possible that up to 1 in 10 sexually active young people are affected. The sex advice charity Brook Advisory Centres believes this is due to the lack of relevant sex education at an early enough stage. To find out more write for a factsheet available free from Brook Publications, 165 Gray's Inn Road, London WC1X 8UD. A teacher's pack, *Infection Protection* (£24.95), is also available from the same address.

© *The Guardian*
December, 1997

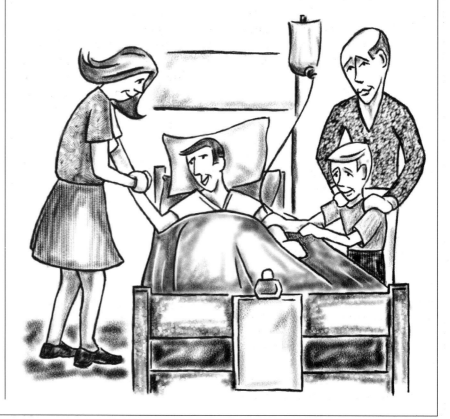

Over 27 million do not know they are infected

Information from UNAIDS

UNAIDS estimates that of the some 30 million people currently living with HIV, the vast majority have no idea they are infected. As with so many other features of the epidemic, when it comes to knowledge of HIV status there is a gaping divide between the developing and industrialised world.

In the United States, the Centers for Disease Control and Prevention (CDC) estimate that two-thirds of people living with HIV know about their infection. In Germany, the proportion of AIDS patients who knew their HIV status at least six months before an AIDS diagnosis remained steady at close to three-quarters in 1994 and 1995. Since 1995, when drugs that can delay the onset of AIDS came onto the market, the proportion has actually dropped to two-thirds. This is because people who knew their status early have already been treated and have been able to delay the onset of AIDS. People who do not know their status are more likely to go on and develop AIDS. The availability of treatment is a powerful incentive to get tested early.

In the developing world, where the epidemic is increasingly concentrated, the picture is very different. HIV testing is done mostly for purposes of surveillance, which involves very small population samples and is done 'anonymously' (with no identification by name of those tested). Few people have any hope of treatment, so they feel little incentive to get tested. But even those who would want to know may not be able to find out. In many countries, there simply are no voluntary testing and counselling facilities; people have no acceptable way of learning if they are HIV-infected. An ongoing study at a rural hospital in South Africa suggests that only 2% of people who are HIV-positive know their status. The situation in urban Kenya seems to be as bad. Of 63 randomly chosen women who tested HIV-positive in one study, just one was already aware that she was infected.

The fact that current testing procedures usually require at least two visits to a test site further complicates access to testing. This can be difficult or expensive for people living in isolated areas. In rural South Africa, just 17% of the people who asked to be tested came back for the result and the advice and support that goes with it. When an on-the-spot test was tried, nearly everyone (96%) chose to know the result.

Since the epidemic is concentrated in the developing world, a conservative estimate might suggest that 9 out of 10 infected people in the world do not know their HIV status. At current estimates, that would suggest there are over 27 million people in the world today who have no idea they are infected.

There are many reasons why HIV testing and counselling for those who want to know their infection status should become part of the broad package of interventions used for AIDS prevention, care and support.

Increasingly, ways are being found to delay symptomatic HIV

A conservative estimate might suggest that 9 out of 10 infected people in the world do not know their HIV status

---

disease including the late stage called AIDS, and to prevent or treat the infections which afflict people whose immune systems have been damaged by the virus. Not all of these treatments are prohibitively expensive.

The earlier people know they are infected, the greater the opportunity for them to access treatment – or put pressure on their communities and countries for improved access, where this is inadequate. Another benefit would flow to individuals and their families. The earlier individuals are aware of their infection, the better they can make informed and responsible decisions about child-bearing, transmission to spouses or partners, and plans for their family's welfare after they fall ill or die.

Perhaps the most important benefit of self-knowledge is that it helps unmask the invisible epidemic and permits a genuine community response.

The experience of the past decade shows that as long as HIV spreads silently and unnoticed, it remains at best a theoretical threat to people and does not get taken seriously. If individuals become aware of their infection early on, while they are still relatively healthy, this would give them the time and energy to support one another as well as alert their community to the epidemic, helping others avoid the disease or cope with its consequences.

However, these benefits to individuals, families and communities are realistically achievable only where people feel safe enough to find out whether they are infected. Efforts by governments and civil society to combat rejection and discrimination directed at people with HIV are vital.

© UNAIDS
January, 1998

13

HIV and AIDS update

Information from AIDS Care, Education and Training (ACET)

World-wide: HIV infection, AIDS, sexual health

New killing fields in Cambodia
HIV is set to cause as many deaths in Cambodia as Pol Pot, according to the WHO. 100,000 Cambodians out of a population of 5,000,000 are already HIV positive, and by the year 2000 over 40,000 will die.
Phnom Penh Post
26 September 1997

AIDS in Africa
- The Director of Harvard University's School of Public Health has warned that careless use of drugs in Africa could lead to the emergence of drug-resistant HIV strains, as it has with malaria.
- Africa has the highest number of HIV positive babies world-wide.
- The $3.5 billion Chad-Cameroon oil pipeline is the first large-scale construction project in sub-Saharan Africa to integrate an HIV/AIDS prevention programme into its design.
- 40 prostitutes in Nairobi have developed a resistance to HIV which is hoped could aid in the search for a vaccine.
- In Tanzania latest estimates suggest 1.35 million people out of a population of 15.5 million are HIV positive.
AIDS Newsletter 1998 13(1)

Teenagers shun safer sex
A national survey in Australia found that half of teenage girls who were sexually active, and 30% of boys, do not use condoms. Distorted reasoning used to justify unsafe behaviour included the suppositions that condom use undermines trust and reduces the excitement of sex. The message that there is no such thing as safe sex also led some to reject condom use as valueless.

AIDS totals
The total recorded cases of AIDS in Uganda now totals 51,779, out of a world total of over 1.7 million. In Africa only Kenya, Tanzania and Zimbabwe have higher officially reported rates. Thailand has reported 59,782 cases. The number of cases which have gone unrecorded remains unknown.

By November 1997 the UK had recorded 14,726 cases compared with 46,032 for France, 110,845 for Brazil and 612,078 for the USA. Spain has the highest incidence in Europe at 46,605
Weekly Epidemiological Record
28 Nov. 1997

UK: HIV, AIDS, sexual health and behaviour

UK – latest figures
By the end of 1997 a total of 15,074 AIDS cases had been reported in the UK, of whom 73% are known or presumed to have died. There have been 31,001 cases of HIV infection.
The AIDS Letter 65

In January 1998 75 new AIDS cases were reported in the UK, 21 of whom died. Between 1993 and 1997 sex between men and women accounted for 29% of all HIV infections – almost a third.
Communicable Diseases Report
27 Feb. 1998

- The number of 14-15-year-olds registered at family planning clinics has trebled in the last 17 years.

- Half of 16-17-year-olds say they have used the morning after pill.
- Around 4,000 under-age girls have abortions each year.
- Britain has the highest teenage pregnancy rate in Europe.
Channel 5 advert

HIV in new-born infants
According to the *British Medical Journal* hundreds of babies are being born with HIV because of failure to detect infection during pregnancy.
- HIV prevalence in mothers rose sixfold between 1988 and 1996.
- Only 15% of previously undetected HIV infections are detected during pregnancy
- Such infections are commonest in London.
- $^3/_4$ of all paediatric HIV infections could be prevented by increased detection.
British Medical Journal Vol. 316

High STI rates in the young
Research by the Brook Advisory Centre found that up to 1 in 10 people under 25 in the UK could be carrying a sexually transmitted infection. Though most young people are aware of the dangers of HIV/AIDS, few are aware of the more common infections.
AIDS Newsletter 1998 13(1)

Oral sex is not safe sex
Recent research in the UK published in the journal *Sexually Transmitted Infections* has confirmed that the HIV virus can be transmitted through oral sex
The Times 17 Feb. 1998

Concern is not behaviour change
A recent survey by Durex found that individuals who expressed concern about AIDS did not necessarily change their behaviour as a result. Whilst 80% of British lovers showed at least some concern about AIDS, less than 20% always practise safer sex.

In the same survey only a third of people were aware that chlamydia is sexually transmitted, and only 13% knew that cervical cancer can be passed on through unprotected sex.

The AIDS Letter 65

Researcher plans live vaccine test

A British AIDS researcher plans to inject himself and up to 20 volunteers with a weakened strain of the live HIV virus to prove that it could work as a vaccine.

Sunday Times 1 Mar. 1998

HIV testing for pregnant mothers

All pregnant mothers in London, Edinburgh and Dundee are to be offered HIV testing in a bid to prevent babies contracting AIDS. In other areas where HIV in women is less prevalent, automatic testing will still not be carried out on the grounds that it would not be cost effective. Some paediatricians challenge this supposition.

Sunday Times 22 Feb. 1998

Syphilis

Monitoring of syphilis indicates a continued slow decline. UK public health laboratories reported 45% of cases were acquired in the UK and 59% of infected people were born in the UK. 25% of infections were acquired in Russia or elsewhere in eastern Europe. Cases in Russia and the Baltic states have been rising extremely rapidly since 1990-91.

Communicable Disease and Public Health 1(1)

Education

Russian Orthodox Church finds sex education immoral

In a recent address to a group of priests and lay people, the Patriarch of the Russian Orthodox Church attacked the immorality of the Russian government's decision to spend $40m on schools sex education.

AIDS Newsletter 1998 13(1)

4-year-old in syringe attack

A 4-year-old boy from Derby was recently given an HIV test after being stabbed with a hypodermic needle in the school playground. He was stabbed by an 8-year-old pupil who found the syringe.

AIDS Newsletter 1998 13(1)

Workplace education succeeds in Zimbabwe

Zimbabwe's Peer Education on HIV Transmission in the Workplace project has seen the number of HIV cases in some industrial areas of Harare fall by 34%. Researchers concluded the strategy is effective and should be adopted permanently by employers.

AIDS Newsletter 1998 13(1)

Call for earlier sex education

In the USA, *POZ* magazine has called for sex education to be provided at an earlier age, since children are reaching puberty younger than before. The effectiveness of abstinence-only education is questioned on practical grounds:

- 75% of teenage pregnancies are fathered by adult males.
- More adult girls are diagnosed HIV+ than boys.
- One in three girls have been sexually abused by age 18.
- 90% of people under 20 with AIDS are girls infected as children by adult men.

AIDS Newsletter 1998 13(1)

Social issues

Prostitute unmasked

Italian authorities identified a 49-year-old prostitute alleged to have had unsafe sex with as many as 5,000 clients despite knowing she was HIV positive. She is to be charged with causing grave personal harm. A newspaper and TV campaign advised her clients to seek HIV testing.

The Guardian 16 Feb. 1998

AIDS generation

Britain's oldest surviving 'AIDS baby', one of more than 400 children born with HIV since the 1980s, is now twelve years old. More than half have already died. Britain is now seeing the emergence of a second

---

By the end of 1997 a total of 15,074 AIDS cases had been reported in the UK, of whom 73% are known or presumed to have died

---

AIDS generation – children growing into adulthood with the virus, facing the prejudice, and discovering their sexuality for the first time.

Sunday Times 15 Feb. 1998

AIDS impacts Generation Xers

According to a recent poll, over half of American 18 to 29-year-olds identify AIDS as the most defining event of their generation, ahead of the Gulf War, the collapse of communism and the Reagan presidency.

AIDS Newsletter 1998 13(1)

Poverty of AIDS patients

Many AIDS patients who spent extravagantly in the expectation of imminent death, but whose lives have been extended by new drug therapies, are facing destitution. For many the return to health means loss of benefits, but jobs are hard to come by. Employers want to know why they haven't been working, and are concerned about long-term health prospects.

The Observer 22 Feb. 1998

Poor targeting wastes money claim

The group Gay Men Fighting AIDS claims that much public expenditure on HIV is wasted through ineffective targeting. Although gay men make up 60% of people living with HIV, only 12-13% of the HIV prevention budget is targeted towards them.

The AIDS Letter 65

Self-esteem increases the risks

Contrary to accepted beliefs, research indicates that higher levels of self-esteem are associated with risky sexual behaviour and more sexual partners.

AIDS Targeted Information 12(1)

Sexual initiation with older partners increases the risk for girls

Compared with girls whose first sexual partner is roughly their age, girls whose first sexual partner is 3 or more years older tend to have first intercourse at an earlier age, are less likely to use a condom at first intercourse, and are less likely to use a condom consistently.

AIDS Targeted Information 12(1)

© ACET 1998

World turned upside down

Living with HIV – a former Westminster University student talks to Wendy Good about the dare that devastated her life

It has been two years since I found out I was HIV positive and, to be honest, it really hasn't sunk in properly yet. It was just so unlikely. I was 18, had just started college and was partying and meeting people all the time. Ironically, despite all the parties, I didn't sleep with anyone, because I was still mad about my boyfriend, Ben, back home.

I lived in a hall in London, with a group of other students, both boys and girls. We all got on really well, but the lads would always try to wind us up by making ignorant or sexist comments. One night, one of them referred to Aids as a 'faggot's disease', which really annoyed me. My friend Jane and I got into an argument which ended up with the lads challenging us to go for a test.

Jane and I needed a woman's check-up anyway, so we booked appointments at a private clinic the following week.

I wasn't at all worried. I'd never done drugs, and I didn't sleep around. I'd slept with three guys, all in proper relationships, and had used condoms. Well, I say that, but, really, when you're on the pill, you tend to forget the rubbers after a while. I mean, who doesn't? I don't know any girls on the pill who use condoms, except for one-night stands. So I suppose I wasn't the most careful.

The day of the test was a laugh. People couldn't believe that we were doing it. But when I saw the doctor and asked him to test for HIV, he made a big deal out of it, asking me why I felt I needed to do this.

I was quite insulted. Just what was he insinuating? He suggested I go for counselling, but I knew that Jane, who was next door, wouldn't, and I didn't want to be left behind, so I refused. The doctor was concerned, but I honestly couldn't see what the fuss was about.

Sitting in the waiting room a week later was a nightmare. I honestly saw my life flash before me, waiting for the results. All I could think about was my family and what would happen if I was positive. But I convinced myself I was just being silly.

When the doctor told me I was positive, my first thought was: 'Oh God, how am I going to tell mum and dad?'

When the doctor told me I was positive, my first thought was: 'Oh God, how am I going to tell mum and dad?' The second was: 'Can't let the guys find out.'

Not exactly rational, I know, but the shock was overwhelming. I didn't cry. I was just numb. I kept saying to the doctor: 'No, no, you must be wrong. People like me don't get this!' The poor man didn't know what to do. He just held my hand as I shook. I couldn't get my head around it.

I walked out to find Jane waiting for me. She just took one look at me and kept saying: 'No, no, oh, God, please no.' When I nodded my head, she burst into tears and gave me a big hug. She started babbling on about getting a re-check and a second opinion, but I knew there was no point.

I felt really strange. I remember being angry at the receptionist for acting as though nothing was wrong. It's a bit like losing your virginity: you think everyone can tell, but they can't. I vaguely remember Jane dragging me into the nearest pub and ordering double vodkas and

shoving fags at me. She wanted to talk about it, but I didn't.

When we got back to the halls, it took the performance of my life to pretend everything was fine, and put up with the lads' jokes about how they wanted to be the next one to sleep with us, so they didn't have to use a condom. I felt really sick when they said that. I suddenly thought: 'Oh, God, I'll never have sex again.'

Eventually, I escaped to my room and tried to cry. But I couldn't. I couldn't even think properly, and ended up going out clubbing that night and having a wild time. I knew Jane was worried about my behaviour, but I didn't care.

The next few weeks were a blur. I carried on with college like every other student, only I went to HIV counselling in the evenings when they were in the pub. I was so lucky nobody but Jane knew, but I couldn't forget about it. Everywhere I went, I saw advertising campaigns I'd hardly noticed before. All the magazines and newspapers were full of it. I woke up every morning wondering how I felt. Did I feel sick? Did I look any different?

When I went home and told my parents, they were great. Well, as good as I could have hoped, really. Mum bawled her eyes out, and dad was his usual, efficient self, saying things like: 'One step at a time, Fay.'

My brother, to whom I'm really close, wanted to do the male thing and go and beat up any guy I'd ever spoken to. I could tell mum and dad were horrified, but they were more relieved when I told them I'd only been with three people. I think dad thought the only straight people who got it were prostitutes.

The first guy I told was Ben. We went for a drink and talked about college and friends and stuff, which drove me mad. In the end, I just interrupted with: 'I'm HIV positive and I have to tell you because you have to get tested.' He just looked at me and said: 'I already have, and I'm positive too.'

The other two tested negative, so I guess Ben infected me. We never did find out for sure which one infected the other. But that's not the point, the fact is I have it and it's not going away.

We never did find out for sure which one of us infected the other. But that's not the point, the fact is I have it and it's not going away

---

I'm living near home now, dad thought it was best that I dropped out of college, which I resent a bit. I'd be in my final year now, not working in a crappy insurance firm as a secretary. I don't know what excuse was given to my friends for dropping out. I'm sure they hate me for not keeping in contact, but I just had to break contact with everyone for a while.

Ben and I live together now and he has been wonderful. Physically I'm fine but I don't kid myself, as Ben has developed full-blown Aids and I know there are some tough times ahead. I suppose I should go on a moral crusade and join in with the educational groups to promote safer sex, but the idea of standing up in front of a bunch of kids saying 'I am HIV positive' just isn't my scene.

It isn't all bad news. I do have new friends and a good social life. The best thing to come from this is how close I've become to my family. So many others in my situation are disowned and I know how lucky I am. This should never have happened to me, I don't fit the statistics so to speak. But as long as I'm allowed to enjoy life I suppose I'll just have to live with it and get on with it.

• National Aids Helpline: 0800 567123

© *The Guardian*
June, 1997

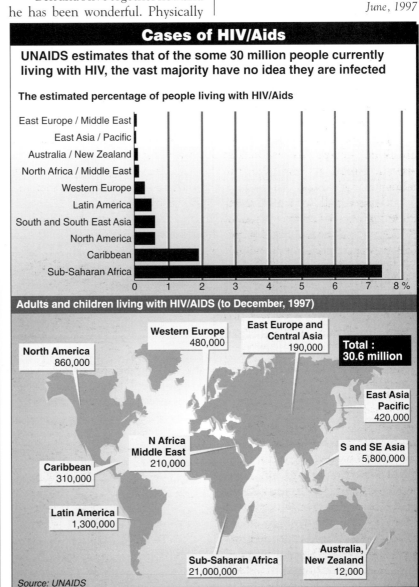

Cases of HIV/Aids

UNAIDS estimates that of the some 30 million people currently living with HIV, the vast majority have no idea they are infected

The estimated percentage of people living with HIV/Aids

East Europe / Middle East
East Asia / Pacific
Australia / New Zealand
North Africa / Middle East
Western Europe
Latin America
South and South East Asia
North America
Caribbean
Sub-Saharan Africa

0 1 2 3 4 5 6 7 8 %

Adults and children living with HIV/AIDS (to December, 1997)

Western Europe
480,000

East Europe and Central Asia
190,000

Total : 30.6 million

North America
860,000

East Asia Pacific
420,000

N Africa Middle East
210,000

S and SE Asia
5,800,000

Caribbean
310,000

Latin America
1,300,000

Sub-Saharan Africa
21,000,000

Australia, New Zealand
12,000

Source: UNAIDS

The history of AIDS

The origins of AIDS

The significance of origins

A clear understanding of the mechanisms by which the AIDS epidemic emerged is necessary if future prevention work is to be directed towards useful goals.

The causes of epidemics are generally related to changes in human behaviours. Microbes frequently change their behaviour as a result of changes in the activities of their hosts. AIDS did not come from nowhere, but arose as a consequence of social changes which permitted the rapid dissemination of HIV.

Understanding how social changes assisted HIV's spread helps us anticipate the future course of the epidemic.

Cases before 1981

AIDS was first identified as a distinct syndrome in 1981 as the consequence of a cluster of cases amongst gay men in large US cities with highly visible and established gay communities. Subsequent review of the medical literature has revealed a plethora of inexplicable AIDS-like illnesses dating back to the late 1940s in the United States and Europe.

Pre-1981 cases fall into two categories: those for which stored blood samples have revealed HIV infection, and those for which no stored blood samples exist, but where the pattern of symptoms reported is nevertheless highly suggested of AIDS.

The oldest AIDS case for which an HIV diagnosis has been confirmed is that of an American youth who died in 1969. The case of a Manchester sailor who was believed to have died of AIDS in 1959 has recently been called into doubt, following the discovery that the strain of HIV isolated from stored tissue samples was virtually identical to strains prevalent thirty years later. US researchers have argued that such a similarity is implausible unless the

An extract from the AIDS Reference Manual 1997

virus was a laboratory contaminant, because HIV would normally mutate considerably during a thirty-year period.

Other early AIDS cases in which HIV has been isolated include a Norwegian family – father, mother and child – who all died in 1976. A Portuguese man who fell ill in 1978 has been retrospectively diagnosed as one of the earliest cases of AIDS caused by HIV-2 (Grmek).

The identified cases in which HIV was present are important because they challenge the belief that HIV is a virus which was introduced into the West in the 1970s. Although some of these cases indicate contact with Africa, the 1969 case of an American youth shows no evidence of an African connection.

Clinical records have also been used to identify pre-1981 cases. Historians have looked for unusual cases recorded in the medical literature which appear to fit the existing definition of AIDS. A surprising number of such reports exist, dating back to at least 1940 in

North America and Europe. Prior to 1960, all the cases identified in North America were men, but thereafter women begin to account for possible cases too, and at least one married couple has been identified (Grmek).

Similar detailed reports do not exist for Africa, except for data concerning Kaposi's sarcoma, which became epidemic in equatorial Africa in the late 1950s. This form of KS, which took the lethal form only in about 10% of cases, was not associated with HIV or with immune suppression, and affected Africans but not Westerners resident in Africa. It has recently been suggested that a number of different forms of KS may exist, perhaps with radically different causes (see *AIDS Treatment Update*, July 1994), so it is as well to be sceptical of the appearance of KS as a marker for the widespread presence of HIV in Africa before the 1970s. African doctors tend to agree that AIDS did not appear in Africa before the late 1970s, and that it became epidemic only in the early 1980s. In the early years of the epidemic the syndrome was known as 'Slim' in Uganda and other central African countries; it first appeared in Uganda on the north shores of Lake Victoria, in Burundi and Rwanda (states to the west of lake Victoria), and in Kinshasa (the capital of Zaire), which lies at the crossroads of trade routes linking East Africa, West Africa, Angola and Zaire.

Isolated cases of AIDS-defining illnesses began to appear among gay men and injecting drug users from the early 1970s in New York and San Francisco. These were not linked by doctors until the beginning of 1981. Although the cluster of PCP cases was identified in 1981, it is possible that a low level of 'pneumonia' cases were treated with standard antibiotics and hence went undetected by the Centers for Disease Control for some years before 1981.

Researchers argue that AIDS cases could have occurred at a low level in the population before the 1940s without exciting much suspicion, because of a greater frequency of infectious diseases. It was only when infectious disease became less common that immune deficiency became more remarkable and worthy of note. Prior to the introduction of antibiotics, tuberculosis and syphilis may have masked minor clusters of HIV disease, in the view of medical historian Mirko Grmek.

Where did HIV come from?

It is often assumed that HIV is a very new virus which has crossed over from animals to humans and spread fairly rapidly. In fact, there are several theories about the source of HIV and the length of time the virus has been present in the human population.

Does HIV come from animals?

HIV is a member of a family of animal lentiviruses (viruses which cause disease slowly). All cause similar immunodeficiency disorders, and infect a wide range of mammals, including monkeys, sheep, cattle and cats. They are species-specific.

It has been established that HIV is a descendant of the simian (monkey) immunodeficiency virus (SIV), which is found in some African monkeys, owing to strong genetic similarities between the two viruses. However, one group of virologists has calculated that the human and simian immuno-deficiency viruses must have diverged at least 140 years ago, undermining the view that HIV is a virus which crossed over to humans from laboratory animals.

Has HIV become more dangerous?

Some scientists believe that HIV may have existed for many years as a relatively harmless virus in humans, but that changing conditions have made it more virulent. The simian immunodeficiency virus (SIV) has been observed to cause progressively more serious disease as it passes through a chain of monkeys, suggesting that adapting to a new host increases the virulence of an

immunodeficiency virus. Conditions which encourage the repeated transmission of retroviruses will therefore encourage the development of progressively more dangerous strains of retroviruses.

When a retrovirus strain has few opportunities to encounter new hosts, natural selection will favour the persistence of strains of HIV which remain in a state of equilibrium with their host in order to continue reproducing itself. It is suicidal for the virus in such circumstances to kill the host. But if a strain of HIV begins to pass through a series of hosts, weaker hosts may allow the virus to grow unchecked and natural selection will tend to favour the multiplication of strains which are highly infectious and more likely to kill the host. In circumstances of frequent transmission to new hosts, virulent and pathogenic strains are just as likely to persist as quiescent, less pathogenic strains.

HIV-1 and HIV-2 serve as examples of divergent strains which may indicate the evolutionary path of HIV. HIV-2 causes disease less frequently than HIV-1, and seems to be more difficult to transmit through sexual intercourse. Until recently HIV-2 was confined largely to Western Africa. HIV-1 may have diverged from HIV-2 some decades ago, and become more virulent as it became more widespread and more frequently transmitted.

Does HIV originate from North America?

Some evidence points to a North American origin for the virulent form of HIV-1.

The HIV epidemic in Africa began slightly later than the North American epidemic, and the predominant strain of HIV-1 which has subsequently spread around the world was first identified in the USA. Other strains have subsequently been identified in Africa.

The epidemic in Haiti, often attributed to contacts with Zaire and used to justify an African origin for HIV, seems to have emerged first of all amongst the contacts of gay and bisexual men and injecting drug users, implying that contacts with North American gay men may have been the route by which HIV entered the Haitian population.

Does HIV originate from Africa?

On the other hand, some of the evidence points to an African source for HIV, not least the tight confinement of HIV-2 to Western Africa until the late 1980s. In addition, the presence of a larger number of genetic subtypes of HIV in Africa compared with anywhere else in the world suggests that the virus has been present for longer in the African population, and has diversified accordingly.

If HIV-1 is a virus which diverged from HIV-2, this must have happened at least 50 years ago in order to account for identified cases of HIV infection dating back to the 1950s.

If the two strains diverged much further back in history, this suggests either that HIV-1 was much less pathogenic in the past, and/or that it was very thinly distributed through the human population outside Africa before the mid-twentieth century, when social changes suddenly permitted the emergence of an epidemic, and that isolated incidents of illness were not recorded or were recorded as outbreaks of tuberculosis and other infectious diseases rather than as a recognisable syndrome.

Another suggestive factor is that many early AIDS diagnoses (from 1959 to the early 1980s) occurred in individuals with connections with Africa, rather than in Europeans without African connections.

Another possibility is that HIV-1 was already present in humans but became more pathogenic at the same time in Africa and North America because social conditions on both continents simultaneously permitted increased transmission. Another example of such simultaneous evolution in nature is the case of the emergence of drug-resistant malaria, which appeared simultaneously in Asia and Africa.

However, it is also important to note that there is virtually no reliable evidence from antibody testing to suggest that HIV was present on a significant scale in African cities before 1981, at least three years after HIV began to appear amongst gay men and drug users in North America. One study could find reliable evidence of HIV infection in only four out of 6,015 serum samples gathered between 1976 and 1984, the period during which HIV was supposed to be spreading widely in Africa, and one of these samples came from a white European (Wendler). This finding is backed up by evidence from studies of blood gathered in Zambia and other Southern African countries, which failed to show conclusive evidence of HIV infection during the 1970s.

On the other hand, a study of blood samples in Zaire showed five out of 659 samples from 1976 to be positive and three of these samples came from individuals who later died of clinical syndromes suggestive of AIDS (Nzilambi). Furthermore, in 1984 Belgian doctors reported 18 AIDS cases, some dating from 1979, amongst Zairois attending hospitals in Belgium (Clumeck).

Could AIDS have been genetically engineered or accidentally disseminated?

Theories regarding the man-made origins of the AIDS epidemic are legion. None stands up to close scrutiny.

Claims that HIV was genetically engineered as a biological weapon are fanciful: until the advent of the epidemic, no scientist had the biotechnological tools necessary to create HIV from known lentiviruses. Conspiracy theories regarding the origins of the epidemic are invariably attempts to apportion blame for the social conditions which permitted

What does HIV do?

The Human Immunodeficiency Virus has a protein coat which binds mostly to one kind of white blood cell called the T4 cell. The T4 cells are an essential part of our body's defences against disease. Once attached to the cell, the virus injects genes to programme the cell to make up thousands of new HIV particles. Eventually the host cell dies and releases all the new viruses into the blood.

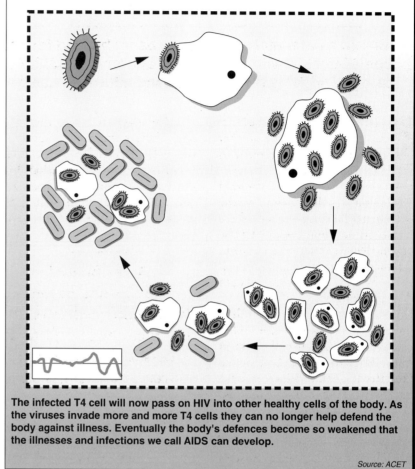

The infected T4 cell will now pass on HIV into other healthy cells of the body. As the viruses invade more and more T4 cells they can no longer help defend the body against illness. Eventually the body's defences become so weakened that the illnesses and infections we call AIDS can develop.

Source: ACET

HIV to become widespread.

It has also been suggested that HIV was accidentally disseminated by vaccination campaigns in Africa during the 1960s and early 1970s. According to this theory, HIV was accidentally incorporated into the vaccine. Seroprevalence studies in Africa do not support this view. If HIV had been disseminated this way, we would expect to find a sudden emergence of high prevalence amongst those vaccinated. This did not occur. However, vaccination may have played a role in other ways: by spreading HIV through un-sterilised equipment, and by 'switching on' latent HIV. During 1986 and 1987 vaccination campaigns in Zaire undoubtedly contributed to the spread of HIV, but live vaccines such as smallpox are also capable of triggering HIV to reproduce in those who are already infected.

Further reading

Richard Chirimuuta: *AIDS, Africa and Racism* (1987)

Nathan Clumeck et al: *Acquired Immunodeficiency Syndrome in African Patients* NEJM 310:8 pp492-497, (1984)

Robert Gallo: *Virus Hunting* (Basic, 1991)

Laurie Garrett: *The Coming Plague* (Farrer, Strauss, Giroux, 1994)

Mirko Grmek: *History of AIDS: Emergence and Origin of a Modern Pandemic* (Princeton University Press, 1990)

Nzila Nzilambi et al: *The prevalence of infection with human immuno-deficiency virus over a ten year period in rural Zaire* NEJM 318:5 pp276-279, (1988)

I Wendler et al: *Seroepidemiology of human immunodeficiency virus in Africa* BMJ 293 pp 782-785, (1986)

© *AIDS Reference Manual 1998*

Pregnant women let down by HIV tests

Britain's antenatal services are being blamed for needlessly allowing babies to become infected with HIV. Jeremy Laurance, Health Editor, examines claims that the care provided by obstetricians and midwives has been 'shameful and negligent'

For the last seven years, the NHS has been counting the number of pregnant women infected with HIV but nothing has been done to ensure more are tested. Despite a 1992 national policy to improve the detection of HIV in pregnancy, there had been no improvement by the end of 1996 when fewer than one in six infected mothers was identified.

The failure has condemned dozens of children to a life of chronic illness and an early death. If a pregnant woman knows she is HIV positive she can halve the risk of transmission to her baby by avoiding breastfeeding and reduce it by a further two-thirds by taking a course of the anti-Aids drug, AZT.

It has been estimated that the number of infected babies in London could have been reduced from 40 to 13 a year if all HIV-infected women had been identified.

A series of nine papers published in the *British Medical Journal* shows that Britain's record is worse than other countries such as France, the US and the Netherlands which offer an HIV test routinely to all women. In Britain, midwives are supposed to offer all pregnant women an HIV test but they often fail to explain why it is important. One paper shows that many women who went to clinics intending to be tested decided against after meeting the 'professionals'.

Anonymous testing for HIV, using blood taken for other tests from which all identification has been removed, has been carried out in antenatal clinics for years to assess the extent of spread of the disease. It shows that between 1988 and 1996 there were 1,241 births to HIV-positive mothers who did not know they were infected. Of these, only 122 were diagnosed while pregnant.

An estimated one in three babies born to infected mothers are themselves infected, unless action is taken to prevent transmission, but the exact number is not known because it can be years before the children are diagnosed.

> ## An estimated one in three babies born to infected mothers are themselves infected, unless action is taken to prevent transmission

---

Pregnant women are routinely tested for syphilis but not for HIV, even though syphilis is far less common. Professor Anne Johnson of the Department of Sexually Transmitted Diseases at University College London Medical School suggests the reason may be 'Aids exceptionalism' – the tendency to regard HIV as different from other infections. She says it is urgent the disease is treated more normally.

In an editorial, Diane Mercey, a senior lecturer in the same department, says compulsory HIV testing is illegal and undesirable but voluntary testing should be recommended to all women.

'The indifference of some obstetricians and an unwillingness by many midwives to broach the issue of testing has meant that Britain has fallen behind other countries in providing pregnant women with access to HIV testing. It is shameful and negligent that we have counted the number of babies at risk of infection since 1990 without acting to reduce their risk.'

© *The Independent*
January, 1998

Global estimates of the HIV/AIDS epidemic

People newly infected with HIV in 1997

Total	**5.8 million**
Adults	5.2 million
Women	2.1 milllion
Children <15 years	590,000

No. of people living with HIV/AIDS

Total	**30.6 million**
Adults	29.4 million
Women	12.2 million
Children <15 years	1.1 million

AIDS deaths in 1997

Total	**2.3 million**
Adults	1.8 million
Women	800,000
Children <15 years	460,000

Total no. of AIDS deaths since the beginning of the epidemic

Total	**11.7 million**
Adults	9.0 million
Women	3.9 million
Children <15 years	2.7 million

Total no. of AIDS orphans* since the beginning of the epidemic	**8.2 million**

* Defined as HIV-negative children who lost their mother or both parents to AIDS when they were under the age of 15

Source: UNAIDS

Aids: why shouldn't mothers be told the truth?

Britain is facing a new Aids epidemic – in children. A growing number of babies are being infected because their mothers have never had an HIV test. Jeremy Laurance, Health Editor, looks at the threat – and how it could be stopped

'Don't die of ignorance' was the slogan once used to alert the nation to the dangers of Aids. Now, the worst infectious condition of modern times is being passed to the next generation – because of ignorance.

Pregnant women who are infected with the virus are being kept in the dark because there is no routine HIV testing in antenatal clinics. More than 250 HIV-positive women gave birth in 1996, the highest number yet recorded. In total, more than 450 babies are known to have been infected, with the oldest survivors now in their mid-teens.

Up to one in three babies born to HIV-infected women become infected themselves, though it may be years before they find out. With a combination of drug treatment and other precautions – avoiding breast-feeding and opting for a Caesarean delivery – mothers can cut their risk of having an infected baby by two-thirds.

Consultants in HIV medicine say too little is being done to protect unborn babies from the disease. A working party of the Royal Colleges of Obstetricians, Paediatricians and Midwives is preparing guidelines on antenatal HIV testing but some doctors fear these will not go far enough. A series of papers on the issue is to appear in the *British Medical Journal* in the New Year.

In some hospitals, the proportion of infected mothers who know they carry the virus is only 2 to 3 per cent

---

Dr Annemiek de Ruiter, consultant genito-urinary physician in charge of women with HIV at St Thomas's Hospital, London, said pregnant women were routinely tested for syphilis but not for HIV, even though syphilis is far less common. Only when their babies were born and then fell ill of Aids-related illnesses did they discover they were infected.

'I get women screaming at me that all this blood was taken while they were pregnant; surely it must have been tested for HIV. But it wasn't. There is a public mis-conception that if blood is taken it is tested for everything.'

Midwives are supposed to offer all pregnant women an HIV test but they often fail to explain why it is important. Dr de Ruiter said: 'It is very much left up to the midwife. We believe it should not just be offered, it should be recommended. It is a shocking thing to learn that you are HIV positive and the women will need counselling but there are now very good treatments we can offer to reduce the risk to the baby. That is a clear benefit.' Anonymous testing for HIV has been carried out in antenatal clinics for years to assess the extent of spread of the disease. Last year 34 HIV-positive women gave birth at St Thomas's but only 14 knew they were carrying the virus. In some hospitals, the proportion of infected mothers who know they carry the virus is only 2 to 3 per cent.

Dr Diana Gibb, a consultant paediatrician at the Hospital for Sick Children, Great Ormond Street, said fewer than 10 per cent of infected women in London were detected during pregnancy. A study of the

cost of testing is expected to show that it is less than the cost of treating the affected children throughout their lives.

'About one in six babies of infected mothers will carry the virus at birth. That rate is doubled if the mothers breast-feed. We now have substantial opportunities to reduce the transmission rate. Something has got to be done.'

By giving the mother the Aids drug AZT during pregnancy and avoiding breast-feeding after birth the transmission rate can be cut from 30 per cent to 5-10 per cent. In France and in the main cities in the United States, most women are tested for HIV and transmission rates are much lower than in the UK.

'I'm very optimistic – I felt my child would be all right'

Gill Hickman was luckier than some. She knew she was carrying the Aids virus when four years ago she decided to try for a baby.

'When I discovered I was HIV positive in 1989 I thought it was a death sentence. Later I realised it wasn't, and that if I had a baby, it wouldn't definitely get ill. I was 38 and I very much wanted a child.'

When Malachai was born she avoided breast-feeding to reduce the risk of transmitting the virus to him. But she turned down the offer of AZT while she was pregnant. 'I am anti-drugs. I wondered what the side effects would be. I am an incredibly optimistic person and I felt really confident that Malachai would be all right.'

He was. He is clear of the virus and mother and child are both well. Ms Hickman believes pregnant women should be offered an HIV test but they should not be pressed into it.

'It has got to be explained sensitively and thoughtfully because the implications are so serious. Women have to think about the implications for themselves as well as their children.'

Some children born with the virus remain healthy for years while others develop serious Aids-related illnesses within months. With the development of new drugs they are surviving longer – to 15 and 16 – but a question mark remains over how long they will ultimately live.

Fear of prejudice means most affected families seek anonymity. Paula Harrowing, of Body and Soul, the Aids charity for families, said children had been bullied and abused at school, and neighbours had turned nasty, after information about their HIV status had leaked.

'One man with an infected child told the neighbours because he wanted support. He came back from work and found the family cat nailed to the door with a note saying "don't come back". Very few of those affected will take the risk of revealing they carry the virus.'

© The Independent
December, 1997

Life imprisonment for 'intentional' transmission

Information from the Vanguard AIDS Newsletter

Legal experts are putting the final touches to a new Bill that will make it a crime punishable by up to life imprisonment for anyone to deliberately infect another with HIV.

It is thought the Bill will be tabled in parliament before the autumn; if passed, it will effectively replace the 1861 Offences Against the Person Act, which has theoretically covered a range of assault charges, including infliction of harm resulting from deliberate infection via sexual intercourse. However, the century-old law has never been successfully applied to cases where people knowingly passed on STDs such as gonorrhoea or syphilis.

Proponents are convinced that the Bill will provide an effective deterrent against malicious and intentional transmission of HIV, especially as it carries a maximum

sentence of life imprisonment for convicted offenders.

The Bill, which had been consulted upon by experts and some AIDS agencies, received fresh impetus last year from the widely publicised case of Janette Pink, the British woman who was infected with HIV during an affair with a Cypriot fisherman. Her successful prosecution became a landmark case.

Proponents are convinced that the Bill will provide an effective deterrent against malicious and intentional transmission of HIV

It remains to be seen just how well the revised legislation stands up in the British court, given the difficulty in proving the 'intention' of an alleged offender. The temptation to profess ignorance of one's serostatus will be strong, for if one did not know whether one had the virus, then how could one be guilty of intentionally infecting the partner? The cumulative effect of that could well be to discourage people from going for HIV test altogether.

Another serious aspect of the new law is that it might put personal relationships under strain, with the prospect of prosecution hanging over couples who might otherwise have felt free to consummate their relationship mutually through sexual intercourse.

© Vanguard AIDS Newsletter
April, 1998

Testing issues

Information from the Terrence Higgins Trust for people thinking of having an HIV test

Thinking of having an HIV test?

This information describes what an HIV test is, and explains where to go and what to expect if you decide to have one. The information raises some issues to think about if you are considering having a test.

It is important to talk to an experienced counsellor or health adviser before you make you decision about an HIV test. Most NHS genitourinary medicine clinics (GUM or STD clinics) and NHS specialist HIV clinics have health advisers who will be able to help you think through the issues.

If you want to talk to someone sooner than that about HIV testing or about anything else connected with HIV and AIDS, phone the Terrence Higgins Trust helpline on 0171 242 1010.

About the HIV test

A test for HIV not AIDS

The HIV test shows whether someone has HIV, the virus which can lead to AIDS. It is not a test for AIDS. AIDS is the name given to a group of medical conditions which may develop when HIV has damaged a person's immune system. For more information on HIV and AIDS, see the Terrence Higgins Trust booklet *Understanding HIV Infection and AIDS*.

Antibodies

The most commonly available HIV test is more properly called an HIV antibody test, because it looks for antibodies to HIV. These are created by the body's immune system if HIV is present.

The window period (sero-conversion)

When someone is infected with HIV, it can take up to three months before

enough antibodies are formed to show up on an HIV test. This gap is called the window period or seroconversion. Throughout the window period, the person with HIV has enough virus in their blood and sexual fluids (and breast milk) to infect another person.

Because the HIV test looks for antibodies, an HIV test less than three months after you became infected might not give an accurate result.

A positive result

If the test finds HIV antibodies, the result is said to be positive. The person is described as HIV antibody positive or HIV-positive. This means that he or she has HIV. It does not mean that the person has AIDS. The test cannot show whether the person is ill, or is going to become ill. Many people with HIV live full and healthy lives for years.

A negative result

If the test does not find HIV antibodies, the result is said to be

negative. A negative test result shows that the person does not have HIV, as long as the test was done after the end of the window period.

An 'equivocal' result

Very occasionally, the HIV test result is equivocal or indeterminate. It is not clearly positive or negative. In most cases this is because the test has found some random antibodies which have nothing to do with HIV.

However, very rarely an equivocal result can occur during the window period. The person has HIV but the HIV antibodies are only just beginning to form.

If the HIV test result is equivocal, the clinic may send the blood sample away for further tests. Or you may be advised to have a repeat HIV test four to six weeks after your equivocal result. In either case, this result is likely to be clearly positive or negative.

Testing for HIV itself

A blood test called an antigen test will find HIV itself if it is present. This test can be used before HIV antibodies have time to form. However, it is very much more difficult and expensive to do than the antibody test. It is not generally available, but may be used in special circumstances. For example, babies born to mothers with HIV are sometimes given antigen tests to see whether they have HIV. This is because antibody tests on babies do not give accurate results.

A second test for HIV itself is the viral load test. It is used to measure the amount of virus in the blood. People living with HIV and their doctors use the information from viral load tests to monitor health and make treatment decisions.

© Terrence Higgins Trust
January, 1998

Aids in US is spreading faster among women than men

Researchers have discovered that Aids is spreading more quickly among women in the United States than among men and that sexual contact – not infected needles – is the leading cause. The new findings offer a gloomy counterpoint to recent happier news on the treatment of Aids. In New York, David Usborne takes a look.

In most of the developed world, at least, the enemy has been in retreat all year. Study after study has shown new success in the prescription of drug cocktails to tame the impact on patients of HIV, the virus that leads to Aids.

Last week, officials in Washington offered this: the Aids mortality rate in America fell 26 per cent between 1995 and 1996. Moreover, the disease lost its crown as the leading cause of death among 25 to 44-year-old Americans. Now it is number two, just behind accidents and a little ahead of cancer.

But this latest report, published in the *Journal of the American Medical Association* and completed by researchers at the Centers for Disease Control in Atlanta, stops the music: there is still no vac-cination and more Americans, especially the poor and dis-advantaged, are getting the virus.

Moreover, the report, which spans 1991 to the end of 1995, shows that the number of those infected is now climbing fastest among American women.

'There has been a lot of attention on the declining death rate; this is the rest of the story,' said Daniel Zingale, who is director of the US advocacy group Aids Action.

The number of women diagnosed with Aids between 1991 and 1995 grew in the United States by 63 per cent compared with an increase of 12.8 per cent for men. By the end of 1995, there were 67,400 women diagnosed with the disease since the epidemic began. Of those, 11,500 were identified in 1995.

Even so, Aids, once dubbed the gay man's plague, is still more prevalent among men than women. In 1995, for instance, the cases of women infected with HIV remained only about 19 per cent of the total for the year.

Attracting particular concern, however, are the behavioural findings behind the statistics. The CDC suggests that while sharing of dirty needles was for a long time considered the principle source of HIV infection among women patients, since 1993 sex with infected men has become the main culprit.

The number of women diagnosed with Aids between 1991 and 1995 grew in the United States by 63 per cent compared with an increase for men of 12.8 per cent

---

By 1995, 52 per cent of Aids cases among women could be traced back to sex with infected men, up from 40 per cent in 1991. By comparison, about 53 per cent of the men who contracted HIV in 1993 did so through homosexual contact. That was sharply down from 63 per cent in 1991. The sexual contact dimension is especially important, the study says, among women under the age of 25. They are $2\frac{1}{2}$ times more likely to catch HIV from sexual contact than by exposure to dirty needles for drug injection.

'It's critical to reach young people before they reach the age of having sex and injecting drugs,' urged Dr Pascale Wortley, the chief researcher on the study. 'The key is, get them before they even start.'

Among the more striking findings in the study was that many adolescent women were contracting the virus through sexual contact with men significantly older than themselves. Moreover, the greater the age-gap, the less likely it was that the woman, often in her teens, would insist on him using a condom.

Mr Zingale of Aids Action insists that this means that while education of young women is important, so too is education of the men that may sleep with them. 'Condoms cost 40 cents. Aids drugs cost $40 a day and may or may not work,' he pointed out.

Researchers also confirmed fears that Aids is spreading fastest in the American Deep South. They suggested that this was caused by an epidemic of cocaine use in the region as well as the pre-dominance, especially among poorer groups, of syphilis.

While the figures in the study do not go beyond the end of 1995, officials have indicated that new statistics due out later this week will confirm the same trends.

© *The Independent*
September, 1997

Aids: and now the bad news

Drug cocktails may ease the Aids epidemic, but they could also kill off any chance of long-term prevention, says Phyllida Brown

You might think that the Aids epidemic is all but over. New cocktails of two or three drugs to treat HIV have slashed death rates by around 40 per cent, closed entire Aids wards, and even made it possible for HIV-positive people to get life insurance. The prospects for people infected with the virus have been transformed.

Transformed, that is, for the 5 per cent of people with HIV who are lucky enough to live in the industrialised West. For most of the 23 million people infected with HIV world-wide, it's a different story. In countries that spend as little as $5 (£3.12) per person on health care each year, drug cocktails that cost $20,000 for a year's course are a sick joke. A vaccine remains the only hope of halting the epidemic in the longer term.

But that vaccine still does not exist and some scientists now fear it may be further away than ever. As better treatments have apparently brought the epidemic under control in the West, the race to press ahead with field trials of today's experimental HIV vaccines is faltering. 'Every day it is more difficult to test vaccines,' says Jose Esparza of UN Aids, the UN joint programme on Aids in Geneva, Switzerland.

Last week, America's National Institutes of Health, which spends $1.5 billion a year on Aids research, held its annual HIV vaccines meeting. In contrast to previous NIH meetings, when plans for field trials dominated the discussions, it was an academic affair, concerned with the finer points of immunology and the latest vaccine studies in monkeys. 'The sense of urgency has disappeared,' said one disappointed international delegate.

Researchers in the US have spent the 1990s inching towards HIV vaccine trials. There have been small-scale studies of the safety of several experimental vaccines against HIV, and test-tube studies of the immune responses that they provoke against the virus. But the ultimate tests – large field trials known as 'Phase III' studies that will show whether a vaccine can actually protect against HIV or not – have yet to happen. There are no active plans for Phase III trials in the US or Europe. And, although small safety studies have been done in Thailand, and a similar study is planned shortly in Uganda, no decisions have been taken or dates set for Phase III trials in either country.

A vaccine remains the only hope of halting the epidemic in the longer term. But that vaccine still does not exist and some scientists now fear it may be further away than ever

---

And the reasons? First, scientists in America and Europe do not yet believe they have found a good enough vaccine. Instead, most are seizing the breathing space that the new treatments have created in the US epidemic to take a step back from the front line. Rather than rush to test the first available vaccines, they are turning to more fundamental research, aimed at building better vaccines that will have a greater chance of success – one day.

'With the heat off, you don't need a quick fix,' says Barry Bloom at the Albert Einstein College of Medicine in New York. Bloom is a member of a high-level committee on HIV vaccines chaired by the Nobel prize winner David Baltimore, which earlier this year advised the US government's HIV vaccine researchers to put more emphasis on basic science.

This makes excellent sense in America, says Esparza, where the epidemic is comparatively small and slow-moving. But – as Bloom acknowledges – it does not answer the short-term needs of countries like Uganda, where the risk of becoming infected with HIV in any given month is twice as high for army recruits as it is for gay men in the US. Yet since about 90 per cent of all Aids research world-wide is American-funded, America's priorities are setting the global research agenda.

In contrast to the US, many developing countries want trials to start now, says Esparza. 'Their perception is that we just don't have the time to get all the scientific information that we wish we could have before we start.' He argues that no one will know whether the available vaccines work or not until they are tested, and that a better vaccine will always lie just around the corner.

The slow pace of research in the industrialised countries is also worrying the pharmaceutical industry, claims Esparza. Companies must develop patented ideas into products within a set time-frame, but cannot do so without trials. 'The companies are really very discouraged,' he says.

Esparza's pragmatic approach is echoed by Rubaramira Ruranga, a major in the Ugandan army and an Aids counsellor: 'It is important that scientists try to get the most appropriate vaccine,' he says. 'But basically, what has been going on should not be stopped unless there is good reason to believe these existing [experimental] vaccines have no potential.'

There is a second, less subtle threat to vaccines from the new treatments. Bloom says that if US politicians think the Aids epidemic is over, they may want to reduce their investment for research into the disease. Just as TB research shrank to almost nothing when the disease seemed to be under control in the industrialised world in the 1960s and 1970s, research on Aids could also be whittled down by the misperception that the disease has been overcome in the US. 'Whenever numbers go down, the money goes away,' says Bloom. 'The real worry is that by the time the scientists get ready to do [trials] the politicians will feel that Aids is getting too much money, and they will put it somewhere else.'

Jonathan Weber, professor of communicable diseases at St Mary's Hospital in London, thinks that although today's experimental HIV vaccines are unlikely to halt the epidemic, they could seriously dent it in countries where HIV is spreading fast. 'The failure to move to Phase III is lamentable because I think that some of the existing approaches might be partially effective,' he says. But fear of failure has prevented scientists from finding out, he says.

On top of these problems, the new treatments make vaccine trials difficult for a third, practical reason

---

The most promising experimental vaccines do not sterilise, but instead keep virus levels so low that they prevent disease

---

– at least in the industrialised countries. The cocktails of drugs make the virus almost impossible to detect in people's bodies, and if you want to find out whether a vaccine is working or not, the one thing you must be able to detect is the virus.

In the early days, scientists believed that the ideal HIV vaccine should block infection completely, just as polio or measles vaccines do. Today, almost no one still believes that this 'sterilising' immunity is possible with HIV. The most promising experimental vaccines – including one in monkeys using a live, weakened strain of HIV's simian relative, SIV, and one based on HIV's naked DNA, rather than the proteins derived from the DNA – do not

sterilise, but instead keep virus levels so low that they prevent disease.

To find out whether such a vaccine works in human field trials, doctors would need to monitor two groups, one vaccinated, the other not, for perhaps three years. If the number of detectable infections and the levels of virus remained consistently lower in the vaccinated group, that would show that the vaccine worked.

But now, in the US, most people who become infected are routinely offered the new drugs. People who participated in vaccine trials could not ethically be denied such treatment. As a result, says Bloom, 'You have no way of knowing whether the vaccine works.'

So then what? Shift trials to countries where the new treatments are unaffordable? That, many researchers believe, would be unethical. All countries would benefit from finding out whether a vaccine works or not. But if the West is not prepared to withhold treatment from people to find out, why should it expect people in Africa, Asia or Latin America to feel differently?

© *The Guardian*
May, 1997

AIDS cases: by year of diagnosis, EU comparison

The rate of new diagnosed cases of AIDS across the European Union (EU) has been declining since its peak in 1994, and in 1996 was 38 per million people. In the United Kingdom there were 16 new cases of AIDS per million population in 1996 which is the lowest number since 1988. Spain has the highest rate of all EU countries; at 105 it was around 45 per cent higher than the next highest country, Italy.

Number per million population

		1986	1991	1996
❶	Spain	12.1	112.7	104.7
❷	Italy	7.9	66.9	72.5
❸	Portugal	3.5	30.0	51.2
❹	France	22.3	79.4	51.0
❺	Luxembourg	7.5	31.2	29.3
❻	Denmark	1.5	40.8	28.1
❼	Netherlands	9.4	29.6	18.4
❽	United Kingdom	8.3	24.0	16.1
❾	Greece	2.4	17.5	15.5
❿	Sweden	6.7	15.9	13.7
⓫	Austria	3.2	25.0	13.6
⓬	Belgium	7.5	25.6	12.7
⓭	Germany	7.3	20.9	9.7
⓮	Irish Republic	1.7	20.5	9.5
⓯	Finland	1.4	5.2	4.1
	EU average	10.1	48.5	38.0

Source: Eurostat: World Health Organisation

Complementary therapies

Information from the Crusaid and STAR Information Exhange

Complementary therapies are those that fall, for the most part, outside the mainstream of conventional Western medicine. They may be used against the symptoms of HIV or to lessen the side-effects of drugs. Some people combine complementary and orthodox treatments in an integrated approach, others choose to use complementary therapies only.

Do complementary therapies work?

Often the worth of these treatments has not been proven in a scientific way. They tend to substitute this scientific proof with a belief or philosophy, and anecdotal evidence is produced to support the claims made by therapists. Not all complementary therapies work for everybody, and not all natural therapies are safe. There is no such thing as a treatment without potential harm, and complementary therapies can be dangerous when used incompetently. The use of a complementary therapy can induce harmful side-effects and complications, or can prevent a clear diagnosis of the effects of orthodox treatment. Some substances can be very potent, so you should be alert to any changes to your body and discuss them with your doctor and your therapist.

Your doctor, your therapist, and you

Whenever considering any change in therapy, complementary or conventional, you should consult your doctor. In this way you will be monitored not only to ensure that the therapy is doing no harm, but also to see how the therapy is working for you. Many complementary therapists have an incomplete knowledge of HIV so it is still important to see your doctor who will know what signs to look out for if you start to become ill. Be wary of doctors who do not take your interest in complementary therapy seriously, and of complementary therapists who tell you that conventional medicines should be avoided. Your doctor and your therapist are there to provide you with care and services. In maintaining a collaborative relationship with them you will be able to get the best of both worlds. A good complementary therapist will know and understand the treatments you may already be on, and will offer therapies to help counteract the side-effects, or increase the beneficial effects, of orthodox treatments.

What follows is a brief overview of the main complementary therapies.

Acupressure is the application of pressure to points around the body in order to balance the different energies which are thought to be required for good health.

Acupuncture is a technique mostly used in traditional Chinese medicine for placing fine needles into points where energy is thought to flow through the body. The needles are meant to stimulate and unblock the energy flowing through these points. Make sure the acupuncturist uses new needles every time. There have been some reports of acupuncture relieving pain associated with peripheral neuropathy.

Aromatherapy is treatment by the essential oils of aromatic plants and spices. Each oil is meant to have a different healing and/or stimulatory effect on the mind and body. The oils can be used directly on the skin with massage, by inhalation, or in baths. A competent aromatherapist must be used as the oils can be very potent and can be associated with serious side-effects.

Autogenics is a therapy where you are taught six basic forms of relaxation to reach a deep state of meditation or near hypnosis. People who conduct this therapy believe that it is possible to 'talk' your body into a state of well-being.

Ayurvedics is a traditional form of medicine and philosophy from India. It incorporates diet, exercise, lifestyle and manipulation of energy points. Clinical trials using ayurvedic formulations for treating HIV are currently under way in India.

Bach flowers therapy was developed in the 1930s for treating emotional well-being. There are 38 flower essences available, the best known being 'Rescue Remedy' which is said to be good for treating shock, distress, anxiety or panic attacks. Bach flower remedies are considered harmless and are readily available from health food shops and some pharmacies.

Chiropractics involves an assessment of your body alignment determined by the position and condition of your spine. Spine and joints are then manipulated to correct any imbalances or misalignment.

Crystal therapy uses different crystals to harness healing energies into different areas of the body. For instance, many crystal therapists believe that rose quartz has significant power to enhance immune function.

Diet, or clinical nutrition, is perhaps one of the more obvious forms of complementary therapy but is often overlooked by people who think their diet is adequate. HIV and related conditions make attention to good dietary intake essential in the ongoing management of your condition.

Exercise: nearly any form of movement which increases your heart rate or muscle tone will generally improve your sense of well-being and reduce stress. Forms of exercise that can be considered are walking, running, tennis, aerobics, weight training or lesser known forms such as t'ai chi or yoga. It is important to start at a pace that is compatible to your general state of health and fitness, slowly introducing your body to exercise so as not cause damage or pain.

Herbalism: many modern-day Western medicines are based on extracts from plants and herbs, but herbalists believe that it is the whole plant or herb itself which is required for an all-round treatment to achieve best results and prevent side-effects.

Homoeopathy uses substances from plant, animal or mineral sources which would normally cause a person to show certain symptoms of a disease. Therapists believe that by diluting down these substances thousands of times they become potent against the disease that causes the same symptoms as the remedy. The concept of this therapy is that 'like cures like' helping the body to rid itself of the symptoms of the disease.

Hypnotherapy helps you enter a deep state of relaxation where the therapist tries to contact the unconscious mind to suggest changes in various mental states (e.g. insomnia or stress). Only qualified hypnotherapists should be consulted, preferably a psychiatrist, psychologist or a doctor who has completed a recognised hypnotherapy course.

Kinesiology was derived by chiropractors in the US and uses a mixture of pressure points and muscle strength tests to gauge a person's general health and balances of energy. Acupressure is then used to correct any perceived imbalances of energy or ill health.

Massage is a widely recognised form of therapy for relaxing, strengthening and stimulating muscles.

Meditation: there are many different types of meditation available. Some simply teach you how to relax or to

reduce stress and improve your feelings of well-being and confidence. There are many books and tapes available to teach yourself the techniques of meditation.

Naturopathy looks at an entire range of diagnostic techniques when assessing a client. The naturopath may look at a person's general health, lifestyle, diet and any symptoms of illness that may be present. The aim of naturopathy is to assist the natural ability of the body to eliminate the cause of ill health.

Osteopathy is a gentler form of chiropractic therapy involving not only the manipulation of the spine, but also the massaging of muscles.

Reflexology uses the stimulation of pressure points in the hands and the feet. Reflexologists believe that 'energy meridians' can be stimulated

to enhance the body's healing properties.

Reiki therapists believe that they can fill their mind, body and soul with a life force energy from the universe. Once filled with this energy, they release it by placing their hands onto different energy centres of the recipient's body.

Shiatsu is a form of Japanese massage aimed at stimulating acupressure points. The philosophy is similar to acupuncture except that pressure is used instead of needles to stimulate various energy points in the body.

Traditional Chinese medicine is a mixture of the benefits of acupuncture and Chinese herbs. It is said to be able to counteract certain symptoms of HIV, and uses herbal mixtures said to have anti-HIV properties.

Visualisation is a technique to 'program' positive thoughts or images to promote good health and healing of the body.

• This information was provided by the Information Exchange. It is available on audio cassette, upon request. If you have any questions regarding this information, you can call the Information Exchange on: 0181 746 5929.

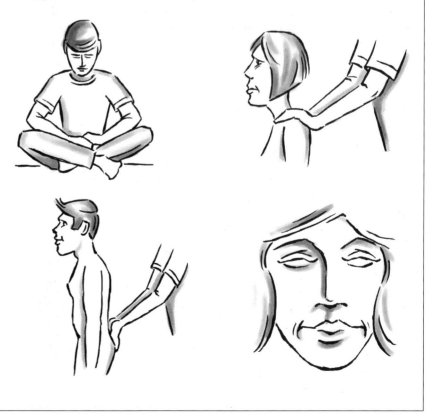

Sexually transmitted diseases

Answers to frequently asked questions about sexually transmitted diseases

Introduction

Sexually transmitted diseases (STDs for short) are very common. They can be prevented and most of them cured with treatment. This information answers questions often asked about STD.

What is an STD?

As the name implies, an STD is a communicable disease that is mainly transmitted through sexual intercourse with an infected person. Although STDs may be caused by a number of micro-organisms, they produce a set pattern of signs and symptoms, such as urethral discharge, vaginal discharge in women, sores in the genital area, lower abdominal pain in women, acute swelling of scrotum in men and enlarged glands in the groin. In some persons, particularly women, the infection my show no symptoms.

Common STDs are gonorrhoea, syphilis, chancroid and non-gono-coccal urethritis. AIDS (acquired immunodeficiency syndrome) is also considered an STD although it can also be transmitted non-sexually.

How does an STD spread?

STDs are mainly transmitted through sexual intercourse which may be vaginal, anal or oral, with an infected partner. The infected partner may or may not have any symptoms or signs and may not know that he or she is infected. Some STDs can also be transmitted through an infected mother to her newborn baby or through deep kissing.

The presence of an STD increases the risk of transmission of HIV, the virus that causes AIDS. A person with an STD but without HIV is more likely to become infected with HIV than a person without an STD. Also, an HIV-infected person

with an STD is more likely to transmit HIV to his or her partner than an HIV-infected person without an STD.

What can happen if an STD is not treated?

An STD may lead to serious complications, if not treated in time:
- It may affect fertility
- It may cause abortion or serious complications during pregnancy.
- Syphilis can cause permanent heart and brain damage.
- Infection may be transmitted to sexual partners.
- An infected pregnant women may infect the baby in the womb or during childbirth.
- HIV will kill the infected person.

Who can get STDs?

Anyone, male or female, young or old, rich or poor, who has sexual intercourse with an infected person may get an STD. The risk of getting an STD increases if one has sex with many partners, has sex with prostitutes or has casual sex relations.

Can STDs other than AIDS be cured?

Yes, if the full course of treatment is taken. It is essential that all medicines be taken as prescribed, even after the symptoms and signs have disappeared. If the course is not completed, the infected will not be cured, a relapse will occur, and the medicines may not work the next time.

The earlier a person with an STD starts treatment, the better it is, in order to be cured quicker, to avoid complications and to prevent passing infection to sexual partners. All infected persons with or without symptoms or signs should be treated.

What should an STD patient do to prevent spreading an STD to others?

People with STDs should abstain from sexual activity until the symptoms and signs have disappeared and the full course of treatment is completed. If they do not abstain, they may spread the infection to their sexual partners. Also, they are more likely to get HIV if their sexual partner is already infected with HIV (remember that a person with HIV may look and feel completely healthy).

If the STD patient cannot abstain from sexual activity until he or she is cured, then a condom must be used throughout the activity, from the beginning to the end.

Is it necessary to treat sexual partners of an STD patient?

Absolutely yes. The STD patient who is seeking care (index patient) became infected by having sexual intercourse with someone who was already infected (source patient). If the index patient is treated but not the source patient, the index patient may be infected again when he has sexual intercourse with the source patient the next time. Similarly, if the index patient, after becoming infected, had sexual intercourse with other partners (secondary contracts), he might have spread the infection to others as well. And the source patient can also infect others if not treated. So all sexual partners must be treated.

Is follow-up necessary?

Yes. The STD patient should return seven days after treatment has ended for a follow-up examination to ensure that he or she is cured or to decide on the next course of action, if necessary. However, the patient may come earlier if the condition gets worse or if there is something that is bothering him or her.

How to avoid STD infection in future

This time it may be a curable STD but next time it may not: HIV is not curable. There fore it is essential to avoid any kind of behaviour that may put one at risk of getting an STD. Premarital and extramarital sex, particularly with prostitutes or different partners, will put one at risk.

The safest behaviour is abstention from sexual activity altogether. Lifelong mutual fidelity to one uninfected partner is also safe. Apart from these, the risk of acquiring STDs can be reduced by engaging only in non-penetrative sexual acts or by using a condom throughout penetrative sexual intercourse.

Any other questions?

If you have other questions or if you wish to get more information about STD, contact a doctor or health care provider or the STD control programme in your country.

Sexually transmitted diseases and young people

- There are more than 1.5 billion young people (between the ages of 10 and 24) in the world today; 85% of them live in developing countries. Between 1970 and 2025, the urban adolescent (between the ages of 10 and 19) population in developing countries will grow by 600%.
- In the least developed countries, only 13% of the girls and 22% of the boys enroll for secondary education.
- Globally, 5 out of every 10 unemployed are young people; in some developing countries it is 8 out of 10.
- 73 million adolescents between the ages of 10 and 14 are working world-wide.

Facts of life

- For the vast majority, sexual relations begin in adolescence.
- Unprotected sexual relations increase risks of unwanted pregnancy and early childbirth, as well as unsafe abortion and sexually transmitted diseases (STD) including HIV/AIDS.
- Lack of knowledge and access to contraceptives as well as vulnerability to sexual abuse puts adolescents at highest risk of unwanted pregnancy.

- In developing countries, maternal mortality in girls under 18 is two to five times higher than in women from 18 to 25.
- World-wide, more than 10% of all births are to women 15 to 19 years of age.
- Adolescent abortions are estimated between 1 and 4.4 million per year, most of which are unsafe because they are performed illegally and under hazardous circumstances by unskilled practitioners.
- Each year more than 1 out of 20 adolescents contracts a curable STD, not including viral infections.

Young people and HIV/AIDS

- There is evidence that new HIV infections in the younger age groups continue to rise as the overall proportion of people living with HIV/AIDS falls.

In 1997 increased numbers of diagnoses were associated particularly with teenage cases

---

- Globally, more than half of all new HIV infections are among the 15-24 age group.
- In most parts of the world, the majority of new infections are in young people between the ages of 15 and 24, sometimes younger. In one study in Zambia, over 12% of the 15 and 16-year-olds seen at antenatal clinics were already infected with HIV.
- Girls appear to be especially vulnerable to infection. Although statistics from Uganda show that, in some areas, infection rates among teenage girls have dropped 50% from 1990, incidence rates are still six times higher than in boys of the same age.
- In South Africa, the proportion of pregnant 15 to 19 year-olds infected with HIV rose to 13% in 1996 from around half that level just two years ago. In Botswana, the infection rate stood at 28% for the same group in 1997.
- Young people may know of the risks of unprotected sex but feel AIDS could not possibly happen to them. In Malawi, most young men and women know how AIDS is transmitted and how it can be prevented. However, many feel invulnerable to the virus. Some 90% of teenage boys said they

were at no risk or at minimal risk of infection, even though nearly half of them reported at least one casual sex partner over the last year, and condom use was low.

Adolescents: greater risks of STD infection

- Experimentation is a normal part of adolescent development which also exposes them to health risks. Young people's sexual relations are often unplanned, sporadic and, sometimes, the result of pressure or force.
- Sexual relations typically occur before adolescents have gained experience and skills in self-protection, before they have acquired adequate information about STDs, and before they can get access to health services and supplies (such as condoms).
- Young girls are especially vulnerable for physiological, social and economic reasons.
- Chlamydia infection during adolescence is more likely to result in pelvic inflammatory disease and, as a consequence, lead to infertility.
- Exposure to infection such as chlamydia during adolescence is more likely to result in cancer of the cervix.
- Stigma and embarrassment associated with STD can impair psychological development and attitudes towards sexuality later in life.
- The diagnosis of STD infection is more problematic during adolescence: the STD may be asymptomatic, especially in

---

Each year more than 1 out of 20 adolescents contracts a curable STD

---

young women; even if adolescents know about existing services, they are often reluctant to seek help for diagnosis and treatment.

Adolescents often have difficulty complying with treatment because it may be lengthy (such as in the case of chlamydia), painful (venereal warts) and sometimes they need to conceal medication so that the STD is not revealed to others.

Sexually transmitted diseases

- Of the estimated 333 million new STDs that occur in the world every year, at least 111 million occur in young people under 25 years of age.
- Sexually transmitted diseases (STDs) are among the most common causes of illness in the world and have far-reaching health, social and economic consequences. In addition to their sheer magnitude, STDs are a major public health problem for two additional reasons: serious complications, and the fact they facilitate transmission of HIV.
- Syphilis was first described in the 16th century. In industrialised countries, syphilis apparently declined during the latter half of

the 19th century. In these same countries, however, there was a sharp rise in incidence after the First World War, but following the Second World War the incidence again fell rapidly, coinciding with the availability of improved diagnostic tests and antibiotics. In some developed countries (France, USA), syphilis began to rise again in the 1960s and has been increasing steadily in some industrialised and developing countries since then.

- Syphilis is the classic example of an STD which can be successfully controlled by public health measures: a simple to use and highly sensitive diagnostic test is available, as is a highly effective antibiotic to which resistance has not developed. If untreated, however, syphilis may lead to nerve damage, arterial wall damage, and mental disorientation, and eventually to death.
- It is generally observed that the incidence of syphilis, as reported by the number of cases treated each year, is highest among the 15 to 30-years-old group and among people with the greatest sexual activity, and that incidence decreases with age. Based on reports of new cases of syphilis treated in Chile in 1993, for example, the highest incidence was among the 20-24 age group, followed by the 25-29 age group. The 15 to 24-years-old group represented 40% of all cases.
- In 1995, it was estimated that there were approximately 12

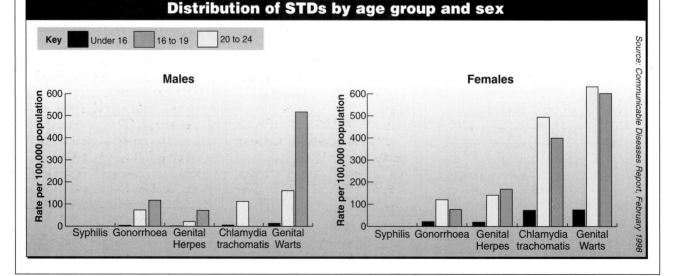

Distribution of STDs by age group and sex

Key ■ Under 16 ▨ 16 to 19 □ 20 to 24

Source: Communicable Diseases Report, February 1998

million new cases of syphilis among adults world-wide, with the greatest number of cases occurring in South and South-East Asia, followed by sub-Saharan Africa.

- Gonorrhoea is a common adult disease, though a significant proportion of those with infection (up to 80% among women and 10% among men) are asymptomatic, that is, they do not have symptoms and therefore they are neither aware of the need for treatment nor of the risk of transmitting the disease to others.

- Infected men usually have symptoms and seek treatment spontaneously. Women frequently have only minor symptoms or are asymptomatic, so detection of infection depends mainly on screening by culture which is costly and requires relatively sophisticated facilities. Few countries operate regular screening programmes and therefore gonorrhoea reporting seldom reflects true levels of infection.

- In 1995, it was estimated that there were approximately 62 million new cases of gonorrhoea among adults world-wide, with the greatest number found in South and South-East Asia, followed by sub-Saharan Africa.

- If untreated, the disease could lead to blindness and infertility.

- Epidemiological research in Western and Central Africa revealed an infertility belt. Up to 45% of women over the age of 45 years have been unable to conceive in that area, due in large part to STD-induced infertility among young women.

- Chlamydial infection, like gonorrhoea, is a common adult disease which has asymptomatic rates in women similar to those for gonorrhoea, but higher rates of asymptomatic infection for men. Like gonorrhoea, chlamydia can lead to pelvic inflammatory disease and infertility. Diagnosis of chlamydia infection is costly and it is not generally available in laboratories in developing countries. Even in industrialised countries, laboratory testing is not universally available. Since many

infections are neither detected nor treated, prevalence rates are high.

- It was estimated in 1995 that 89 million new adult chlamydia infections occurred in the world with the greatest numbers in South and South-East Asia, followed by sub-Saharan Africa.

- Recently developed laboratory tests have, however, made screening programmes for chlamydia infection possible in some industrialised countries. Rates of infection among women attending family planning clinics from 1989 to 1993 in the United States of America, for example, have been shown to vary from 4.5% to 8.5%.

- Trichomoniasis is one of the most common STDs. It causes symptoms in approximately 50% of infected women. In men, infection is usually of short duration but men easily transmit the parasite responsible for the disease to their partners.

- Studies in Malawi and in former Zaire have shown association of the disease with HIV seroconversion in women. These findings, along with high prevalence of the disease world-wide, call for greater attention to this medical condition, for which diagnosis is simple and treatment is effective.

- Prevalence rates among African women attending antenatal clinics range from 12% in Kenya to 47% in Botswana.

- Approximately 170 million new cases of trichomoniasis were estimated to occur in the world in 1995.

- No estimates of chancroid were made using the methodology developed for other STDs. Poor understanding of the epidemiology and natural history of the disease and the absence of a good test make it difficult to estimate prevalence and duration of infection.

- The genital ulcers produced by chancroid are a major risk factor for HIV transmission, and the incidence of chancroid varies greatly between countries and regions. For example, in Swaziland and Kenya, 44% and 62% respectively of genital ulcers were diagnosed as chancroid in STD clinics in 1980. In western Algeria, chancroid is the most common STD observed and the primary cause of genital ulcer disease. In India, in 1989, chancroid represented 26% of all reported STDs. In most industrialised countries chancroid has become a rare disease.

© World Health Organisation 1998

Warts and all

Anita Weston outlines the current situation concerning sexually transmitted infections in the UK

In our world of around six billion people, increasing numbers of men, women and children contract sexually transmitted infections (STIs) every year. In 1995 alarm bells were sounded when the World Health Organisation (WHO) issued a press release in which it was estimated that over a third of a billion new sexually transmitted infections would occur in that year alone. This information focused only on infections that were potentially curable and underestimated the real size of an evolving pandemic of STIs that continues to expand.

Every STI could potentially be a new HIV infection, as STIs are an indication that unprotected sex has taken place. Therefore, increasing numbers of STIs are fuelling the spread of HIV. The presence of inflammation or genital lesions greatly increases the risk of sexual transmission of HIV.

STIs may cause infertility. For women STIs may cause many serious complications, such as pelvic inflammatory disease and ectopic pregnancy. Many STIs can be passed on to infants during pregnancy and childbirth. Their effects include abortion and still-birth, and eye infections and pneumonia in the newborn.

Facing the facts

In the UK the number of new cases of STIs is rising, especially chlamydia, genital herpes and genital warts.

In 1995 alarm bells were sounded when it was estimated that over a third of a billion new sexually transmitted infections would occur in that year alone

---

The findings of the Durex Global Sex Survey suggest that the practice of safer sex is being forgotten (Durex, 1997). It found that people are having more sex than ever before, with the French being the most sexually active, having an average of 151 episodes of sexual intercourse per year. The UK figure is 113 times per year. Those interviewed believed sexual satisfaction to be more important than concerns over STIs, HIV or unwanted pregnancy.

Only 25% of the UK respondents said they put great importance on not contacting or spreading HIV during sexual intercourse, and just 3% said they were concerned about other STIs.

Finally, the survey called for a greater responsibility from the medical and nursing professions for sex education – of the 10,000 adults questioned in 14 countries, only 2% cited doctors and nurses as a source of information.

The hidden problem

Clarke carried out an international study to explore awareness of STIs (Clarke, 1995).

Only 1% of the 959 UK citizens interviewed had heard of chlamydia and 2% had heard of genital warts.

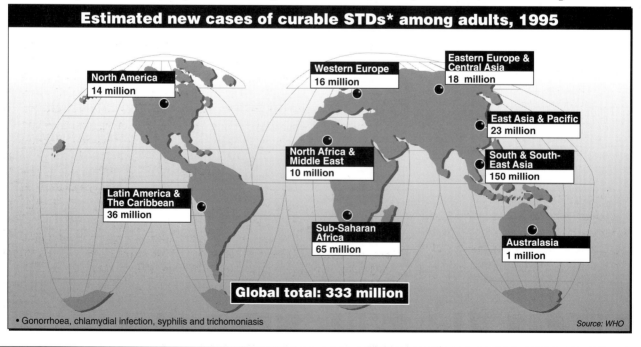

Estimated new cases of curable STDs* among adults, 1995

North America: 14 million
Western Europe: 16 million
Eastern Europe & Central Asia: 18 million
East Asia & Pacific: 23 million
North Africa & Middle East: 10 million
South & South-East Asia: 150 million
Latin America & The Caribbean: 36 million
Sub-Saharan Africa: 65 million
Australasia: 1 million

Global total: 333 million

• Gonorrhoea, chlamydial infection, syphilis and trichomoniasis

Source: WHO

Considering that these two infections are the most common STIs in the UK, this finding is extremely worrying and suggests that public health promotion campaigns targeting STIs should become a government priority.

Cases of gonorrhoea declined between 1992 and 1994, but there has since been a gradual increase in the numbers of cases being seen in genitourinary medicine (GUM) clinics. There was an increase of 5% in 1995 (12,359 cases) over 1994 (DoH, 1996).

A report last November suggested that the UK is facing a new epidemic of herpes simplex virus. Government statistics allegedly reveal an increase in the incidence of genital herpes of 50% in the past decade, with more than 27,500 cases reported last year (Adler, 1997). Research suggests that one in five of the population could be infected by the incurable virus.

Chlamydia trachomatis is the most common bacterial STI seen in this country. It causes non-specific urethritis in men and, if left untreated, may cause epididymitis and infertility. Chlamydia infects the female cervix and may go unnoticed in an infected woman because often there are no symptoms. However, if left untreated chlamydia can lead to pelvic inflammatory disease and infertility.

It is precisely because infections such as chlamydia and gonorrhoea can be virtually hidden, particularly in women, that a sexual health check-up at a GUM clinic is recommended if there is a change of sexual partner or for those who have more than one sexual partner. The same recommendation should be made for men, although men with a bacterial sexually transmitted infection usually display more obvious symptoms.

Promoting sexual health

An effective sexual health promotion strategy which we could learn from is that produced by the National Institute of Public Health in Stockholm, Sweden. The institute has the responsibility of coordinating STI and HIV prevention in Sweden. It works closely with central and local

---

Through systematic preventive measures the Swedes have successfully reduced the frequency of many STIs

---

government agencies and the community and maintains international links with the United Nations and European Union AIDS programmes.

The institute's policy is that sexual activity is an important component of life, and therefore, it inculcates a positive view of sex and personal relations. The Swedes believe that knowledge of STIs and HIV and how they are transmitted can help allay the fears many people feel about discussing them. Through systematic preventive measures the Swedes have successfully reduced the frequency of many STIs.

Ignorance is the enemy

The incidence of STIs will continue to increase unabated while people remain ignorant about the facts. This ignorance is also a problem for many

health care workers who are often in the dark when it comes to knowledge of STIs and how best to advise clients about these infections.

References

Adler, M.W. *Sexual health: A Health of the Nation failure*. British Medical Journal 1997; 314: 7096, 1743-1747.

Clarke, P. *Awareness of Sexually Transmitted Diseases. An International Study*. New Orleans, La.: Society for Sexually Transmitted Diseases Research, 1995.

Department of Health. *Statistical Bulletin: Sexually Transmitted Diseases, England 1995, Bulletin 1996/14*. London: DoH, 1996.

Durex *Global Sex Survey 1997*, London: London International Group, 1997

Anita Weston, RGN, MSc, Cert Ed, Cert Counselling Skills, PGC Applied Research Methodology, is associate Dean, School of Health Community and Social Policy, Wolfson Institute of Health Sciences, Thames Valley University, London.

© Nursing Times January, 1998

Screening for sexually transmitted disease

Women at risk of a sexually transmitted disease known to be a major cause of infertility are to be screened in an effort to halt its spread, the Government announced yesterday, writes Jeremy Laurence.

Sexually active women under 25 and those over 25 who have changed partners will be offered a test for chlamydia, the commonest sexually transmitted disease which accounts for almost half of all ectopic pregnancies. GPs will be asked to inquire about sexual histories of their female patients and offer the test, which can be conducted on a urine sample where appropriate. All women seeking abortions and attending genitourinary medicine clinics, among whom infection rates are higher, will be tested.

Chlamydia is often impossible to detect until it is too late, resulting in infection, causing irreversible damage to the reproductive tract. If identified early, it can be easily cured with a single dose of antibiotics provided both partners are treated.

In Europe, screening is commonplace and has led to a sharp fall in the incidence of infertility. Tessa Jowell, minister for public health, said pilot screening programmes would be launched in Portsmouth and Wirral later this year.

© The Independent May, 1998

Young people's sexual attitudes and behaviour

A review of research

When does it all begin?

Children gather information and attitudes about sexuality much as they do about everything else, that is, during their general socialisation process and as a natural part of their exploration of their world. Anecdotal evidence from parents has found that children generally begin to be curious and ask questions about sexuality from about the age of three. Children pick up attitudes and information about sexuality from their parents and carers and the world around them long before formal sex education begins. This is confirmed by research[1] which has shown that we consistently underestimate children's awareness of human sexuality. In their comprehensive study of children aged from 5 to 15, the Goldmans found that pre-adolescents were conscious of divorce, homosexuality, rape, child abuse, pornography and prostitution. More recent research[2,3] highlights how primary age children 'practise' for adult sexuality through the playing of games such as kiss chase; acting out current media programmes; role playing adult roles; 'going out'; gossip about other pupils and teachers and approval or disapproval of certain behaviours.

Changes in sexual behaviour

The most comprehensive survey of Britain's sexual attitudes and lifestyles was published in 1994.[4] It highlighted a number of important changes in sexual behaviour over the last 50 years.

Young people at the start of the 1990s were becoming sexually active some four years earlier than those in the early 1950s. Median age at first intercourse (the age by which half of young people have experienced first intercourse) has fallen by four years for women from 21 to 17, and by three years for men, from 20 to 17

over the past four decades. However, contrary to popular belief, this did not occur during the 1960s. The biggest drop occurred during the 1950s, the age at first intercourse fell as much during this one decade as it did over the next thirty years.

Research[5] with gay young men found that the average age of first homosexual experience was 15.7. Some 10 per cent realised they were gay before they were 10 years of age, and the majority (86 per cent) did so before they were 20. The average age difference between partners at first sex was one year. The *National Survey of Sexual Attitudes and Lifestyles* found that by contrast for women their first homosexual experience is likely to occur fairly consistently at any age (up to 50).

The decrease in age at first intercourse over the past 30 years is equally marked for age at first sexual experience. The median age for first sexual experience has dropped from 16 to 14 for women and from 15 to 13 for men (comparing age groups 45-59 to 16-24).[4]

There has also been an increase in the number of young people who have sexual intercourse before the age of 16.[4] Nearly one in five women and more than one in four men under the age of twenty have had intercourse before the age of 16 for those age 16-24, compared with fewer than one per cent of women and little more than one in 20 men in the previous generation.

The survey[4] found that premarital sex has become the norm for both women and men. Fewer than one per cent of women in the age group 16 to 24 had their first sexual experience within marriage, and no men at all did so, compared with 38.5 per cent of women and 14.2 per cent of men in the 45 to 59 age group.

The gap between the age at which young women have sexual intercourse for the first time and that of young men has been closing. For those aged 25 and over, the median age for men is one year earlier than it is for women, whilst for those under the age of 25 it is the same for both sexes.

The age of first intercourse doesn't vary significantly between developed countries. The acceptance of teenage sexual activity in the Netherlands has not led to earlier sexual intercourse; Dutch teenagers start having sex at 17.5 years, slightly later than their British counterparts.[6]

These major changes in behaviour have implications for the provision of sex education and should encourage teachers to provide appropriate education before young people become sexually active.

Attitudes towards sex

Attitudes towards sexual behaviour have changed in some ways too. For instance, there is widespread support among young people for cohabitation as an alternative and as preparation for marriage.[7] A 1996/7 survey[8] of 3,000 16 to 18-year-olds asked the question 'Do you consider that it is morally wrong to make love to someone with whom you are in a long-term relationship when you are not married?' 80 per cent of Anglican respondents, 85.4 per cent of Roman Catholics; 66.7 per cent of other Christians; and 81.1 per cent of other religions (including Muslims, Jews and Hindus) said no. Another survey found that a loving relationship was seen by the majority of young people as very important or important when people have sex (86 per cent).[9]

Reasons for not having sex

One survey found that for girls and boys who had not been sexually active, around about half said this was because they hadn't met the right person (54 per cent girls and 47 per cent boys).[10] Girls are twice as likely to say they aren't ready (43 per cent girls and 22 per cent boys), but boys are twice as likely to feel that the main reason is lack of opportunity (40 per cent boys compared with 19 per cent girls).

Reasons for first sex

Among other reasons such as 'natural follow-on', being in love, and curiosity, young people cite peer pressure as one of the main factors precipitating first intercourse. Although girls are more likely to feel pressured by their boyfriends, surveys show that young men are twice as likely as young women to feel pressured by their friends.[4,10]

Factors associated with early sexual intercourse

Although 'cause and effect' relationships are difficult to disentangle when researching into sexual behaviour, a number of factors have been found to be associated with early sexual experience.[11] These include: very early sexual experience, early puberty, family structure, child abuse and poor educational attainment. Certain groups of young people are particularly vulnerable. Many young people in the care system ('looked after') for instance will have had inadequate or damaging life experiences which can leave them with low self-esteem and lacking the necessary skills and confidence to negotiate personal relationships. In a 1992 study,[12] researchers found that 25 per cent of young women were mothers by the time they had moved to independence or ceased to be looked after. This contrasted with a national figure of 3 per cent for the 16-19 age group. A 1986 Streetwise Youth Project Report[13] stated that two-thirds of male sex workers interviewed had been looked after by a local authority.

Factors associated with delayed sexual intercourse

Parental attitude towards sexual matters has been found to be a strong factor associated with timing of sexual experience. In Ingham's

survey[14] the researchers found that in those families where sexual matters were talked about openly and with a 'realistic' approach, children were less likely to have had their first experience of sexual intercourse under the age of 16, compared with families who either didn't talk about sexual matters, or used a 'moralistic' approach and were strongly opposed to sex outside marriage.

School sex education has also been found to be a factor in timing of sexual experience. Welling's survey found that boys who cited school as their main source of information on sexual matters were less likely to have first experience of sexual intercourse before the age of 16 than those who cited friends as their main source.[15] The same survey found that those who cited school as their main source of information were more likely to have used some form of contraception, notably a condom, at first intercourse.

Regret associated with sexual experience

Early sexual experience is more likely to be associated with regret. The younger the age at first intercourse, the higher the percentage who feel they had sex too soon.[4] However there are marked gender differences. More than half of women (58.5 per cent) for whom first intercourse occurred before the age of 16 judged this to have been too soon, but less

than a quarter of men did (24.4 per cent). Qualitative surveys have suggested that young men are more likely to perceive their first sexual experience as positive than young women.[16,17] This may be due to different expectations of the experience, or a 'rites of passage' effect for young men.[18] A survey of 13 to 16-year-olds in London, Birmingham and Newcastle areas[9] found that sexual experiences were regretted due to: the influence of drink or drugs (43 per cent boys, 9 per cent girls); it happening in the heat of the moment (33 per cent and 40 per cent); they thought it would be different (16 per cent and 20 per cent); or they felt pressured (8 per cent and 31 per cent).

Unsupported sexualities

Certain groups of young people are particularly unsupported with regards to their developing sexualities. These include gay young men and lesbians and young people with disabilities. A Stonewall survey[19] of lesbians, gay men and bisexuals found particularly high levels of homophobic violence, harassment and verbal abuse amongst those aged under 18. 48 per cent of respondents under 18 had experienced violence, 61 per cent had been harassed and 90 per cent had been called names because of their sexuality. 40 per cent of these attacks had taken place at school. Other qualitative surveys[20,21] document the negative effect these experiences have on the self-esteem of this group of young people.

The situation is different for young people with disabilities. Their sexuality has traditionally been viewed as non-existent or as problematic. Their experiences and views are largely absent in surveys of sexual behaviour (one reference in the National survey[4]). The little research that does exist presents a picture of high levels of abuse,[22] high incidence of HIV infection[23] and little sex education from parents and carers or school-based sources.[24] This situation is gradually changing with the passing of the Education Act 1993[25] which granted children with disabilities an equal right to school-based sex education.

Sexual health of young people

The sexual health and consequently the sexual behaviour of young people remains a key health priority for government.[26] The UK has one of the highest rates of teenage conceptions (under 16) in Western Europe.[27] In addition, abortion rates are high, sexually transmitted infections are on the increase amongst young people and the incidence of HIV infection remains unacceptably high.[28] Young people having first sexual intercourse under the age of 16 are the least likely to use contraception and report higher numbers of sexual partners over time.[4] Contraception use also has implications for the incidence of sexually transmitted infections which can have long-term health consequences. Surveys of young people show low levels of awareness of common sexually transmitted infections such as chlamydia,[29,30] and little perception of themselves being at risk of infection.[31]

Sex education

The most reliable research available shows that sex education does not encourage or increase sexual activity amongst young people.[32] A review of national and international research[11] shows that school-based sex education can be effective in reducing teenage pregnancies, particularly when linked to access to contraceptive services. A major research study in Scotland is currently further investigating the links between sex education provision and sexual attitudes and behaviour.[33] The provision of good quality personal and social education including sex education has been included in the Government's plans for improving standards in schools.[34]

Caroline Ray – Sex Education Forum

References
1 Goldman, R & Goldman, J (1982) *Children's Sexual Thinking.* Routledge & Kegan Paul.
2 Epstein, D (1997) 'Cultures of schooling/cultures of sexuality,' *International Journal of Inclusive Education.* 1,1,37-53.
3 Redman, P (1996) 'Curtis Loves Ranjit: Heterosexual masculinities, schooling and pupils' sexual cultures.' *Educational Review,* 48,2,175-182
4 Wellings, K and others (1994) *Sexual Behaviour in Britain: The National Survey of Sexual Attitudes and Lifestyles.* Penguin.
5 Weatherburn, P and others (1992) *The Sexual Lifestyles of Gay and Bisexual Men in England and Wales.* Project SIGMA.
6 Jones, E and others (1985) 'Teenage Pregnancy in Developed Countries: Determinants and policy implications.' *Family Planning Perspectives.* 17, 2, 53-63.
7 Roberts, H and Sachdev, D (1996) *Young People's Social Attitudes – Having Their Say: The views of 12-19 year olds.* Barnardo's.
8 Vardy, P (1997) *The Puzzle of Sex.* Fount Paperbacks.
9 Oasis Trust (1996) *Teenagers and Sex: Education, attitudes and pressures.*
10 Heath Education Authority (1992) *Today's Young Adults: 16-19 year olds look at diet, alcohol, smoking, drugs and sexual behaviour.* HEA.
11 NHS Centre for Reviews and Dissemination (1997) 'Preventing and Reducing the Adverse Effects of Un-intended Teenage Pregnancies.' *Effective Health care Bulletin,* Vol.3, No 1.
12 Biehal, N and others (1992) *Prepared for Living? A survey of young people leaving the care of three local authorities.* National Children's Bureau.
13 Streetwise (1986) *Youth Prostitution: A balance of power.*
14 Ingham, R (1997) *The Development of an Integrated Model of Sexual Conduct Amongst Young People.* ESRC Project. Department of Psychology, University of Southampton.
15 Wellings, K and others (1995) 'Provision of Sex Education and Early Sexual Experience: The relation examined.' *British Medical Journal,* 311, 7002, 414-417.
16 Thomson, R and Scott, S (1991) 'Learning About Sex: Young women and the social construction of sexual identity.' *Women Risk & AIDS Project Paper 4.* Tufnell Press.
17 Holland, J, Ramazanoglu, C and Sharpe, S (1993) *Wimp or Gladiator: Contradictions in acquiring masculine sexuality.* WRAP/MRAP Paper 9. Tufnell Press.
18 Holland, J, Thomson, R and Ramazanoglu, C (1996) 'In the same boat? The gendered (in)experience of first heterosex.' In *Theorising Heterosexuality. Telling it straight.* Buckingham Open University Press, pp 143-161.
19 Mason, A and Palmer, A (1996) *Queer Bashing: A national survey of hate crimes against lesbians and gay men.* Stonewall.
20 Springham, N (1996) *Telling Tales: An exploratory study of young gay men's experiences of schooling on Tyneside.* Newcastle and North Tyneside Health promotion.
21 Trenchard, L and Warren, H (1984) *Something to Tell You.* London Gay teenage group.
22 Westcott, H (1991) 'The abuse of disabled children: a review of the literature.' *Child: Care, Health and development,* 17, 4, July/Aug, 243-258.
23 British Deaf Association (1995) *Survey of Deaf People's Health Habits.*
24 Buckley, S and Sacks, B (1987) *The Adolescent with Down's Syndrome: Life for the teenager and for the family.* Portsmouth Down's Syndrome Trust.
25 *Education Act 1993* (1993) HMSO.
26 Warden, J (1997) 'Public Health Strategy Will Tackle Inequality in England', *British Medical Journal,* 314, 7100, 75.
27 Conceptions in England and Wales 1995 (1997) *Monitor* FM1 97/2. Office for National Statistics.
28 Adler, M (1997) 'Sexual Health – A Health of the Nation failure.' *British Medical Journal,* 314, 7096, 1743-1747.
29 Winn, S, Roker, D, and Coleman (1995) 'Knowledge About Puberty and Sexual development in 11-16 Year Olds: Implications for health and sex education in schools.' *Educational Studies,* 21, 2, 187-201.
30 Health Education Authority (1996) *AIDS Awareness 2* (Combined) February/March 1996. BMRB on behalf of the HEA. Unpublished. Cited in Health Education Authority (1997) *Health Update: Sexual Health.*
31 *Health Monitor* (1997) NOP Report for Durex.
32 Kirby, D and others (1995) 'School Based Programmes to Reduce Sexual Risk Behaviours: A review of effectiveness.' *Public Health Reports* (US) 109, 3, 339-360.
33 Wight, D and others (1996) 'From Theory to Practice: Developing a theoretically-based teacher-delivered sex education programme' in *Sexual Awakening: Making sex education work.* Proceedings of the Symposium held on Wednesday 3 April 1996. Medical Research Council.
34 Department for Education and Employment (1997) *Excellence in Schools.*

• The above is an extract from *Sex Education Matters,* produced by the Sex Education Forum within the National Children's Bureau. See page 41 for address details.

Sexually transmitted infections

How to prevent them and where to go for help

What are sexually transmitted infections?

During sexual contact infections can be passed from one person to another. These are known as sexually transmitted infections (or sexually transmitted diseases). Anyone who is having sex can get a sexually transmitted infection from an infected partner if they do not use any protection.

It is important to realise that:
- Many sexually transmitted infections have no obvious symptoms of illness, so you could have an infection and not know it.
- Sexually transmitted infections occur frequently in both men and women.
- Many sexually transmitted infections are curable and all are preventable.
- Delaying treatment could mean that the infection gets worse and other problems could occur.
- A mother can pass on an untreated infection to her child during pregnancy and birth.

Types of sexually transmitted infections

There are many types of sexually transmitted infections:

Common
- Genital warts
- Chlamydia
- Non-specific urethritis (NSU)
- Genital herpes
- Gonorrhoea (or the clap)

Less common
- Trichomonas vaginalis (TV)
- Syphilis (the pox)
- HIV (Human Immunodeficiency Virus)
- Hepatitis B and C
- Infestations, including scabies and pubic lice (crabs)

Some of these infections are very serious. For example, HIV is the virus which causes AIDS. Hepatitis B can cause liver problems such as cirrhosis (scarring) or liver cancer. Syphilis can cause permanent damage to the heart, brain and nervous system if left untreated.

Other infections are occasionally, but not always, spread through sexual contact. These include thrush, bacterial vaginosis and cystitis.

How are these infections spread?

Sexually transmitted infections are usually spread when infected blood, semen or vaginal fluid come into contact with another person during sex. But some infections (such as HIV and hepatitis B and C) can be spread through infected blood, when needles and other injecting equipment are shared.

Different infections can be passed on to either partner through different sexual activities:
- Chlamydia, NSU, gonorrhoea, hepatitis B and HIV infections are usually spread through penetrative vaginal, anal or oral sex (when the penis enters the vagina, anus or mouth).
- TV is spread by vaginal sex, and though men may carry it, they usually do not have any symptoms. It can be passed on by sex between women if fluid from the vagina is exchanged – by sharing sex toys, for example.
- Genital warts, herpes and syphilis can be spread through body contact between partners' genital areas. Because these infections can occur on or in the mouth, they can also be spread by oral sex when someone uses their mouth or tongue to stimulate their partner's genitals.
- Scabies, crabs and other infestations can be spread by any of these sexual practices and also by skin contact.

How do I know if I have a sexually transmitted infection?

People who have a sexually transmitted infection sometimes get symptoms to show that something is wrong. But often they don't.

Some warning signs to look for are:
- An unusually thick or watery, cloudy or smelly discharge from the vagina (not to be confused

with the normal slight discharge which all women have).
- A discharge from the penis.
- Itching, rashes, sores, blisters or pain in the genital area.
- A pain or burning sensation when you pass urine.
- Urinating more than usual.
- Pain during sex.

But remember:
- Sometimes there are no symptoms.
- Symptoms may not appear for months.
- Symptoms may disappear when there is still infection.
- You can have more than one sexually transmitted infection at a time.

Untreated sexually transmitted infections can cause serious and permanent damage. Get yourself checked out straight away if you have any of the symptoms listed above or if you think your current or a recent partner has an infection.

Go to your own GP or any NHS sexual health clinic, often called STD (sexually transmitted disease) or GUM (genito-urinary medicine) clinic.

What if I don't have treatment?
Some sexually transmitted infections can cause permanent damage to your health if left untreated. They can cause:

In women
- Pelvic pain which may recur throughout life.
- Damage to the fallopian tubes (the tubes which carry the eggs from your ovaries to your womb). This may lead to an ectopic pregnancy, when the fertilised egg begins to grow in the fallopian tube or outside it, rather than in the womb.
- Infertility.

In men
- Inflammation (pain and swelling) of the testes.
- Inflammation of joints and eyes. (Women may also experience this.)
- Reduced fertility.

AIDS is currently incurable. New treatments for HIV show promise, but it is still too early to say what their impact will be. There are treatments for many of the illnesses that people with HIV may get. If you have another untreated sexually transmitted infection, you increase the risk of getting HIV or passing HIV to your partner.

Where do I go for help?
If you think that you might have a sexually transmitted infection you should go to an NHS sexual health (GUM) clinic. These clinics offer free check-ups and treatment for sexually transmitted infections. They also do HIV testing. All information is kept strictly confidential. You can go to any clinic, anywhere in the country. You don't have to use a local one and you don't have to be referred by your GP.

You can find details of your nearest NHS sexual health clinic in the phone book under genito-urinary medicine (GUM), sexually transmitted disease (STD) or venereal disease (VD). Or you could ring the National AIDS Helpline free on 0800 567 123 for details of local clinics, or phone your local hospital and ask for the 'special' or GUM clinic. (Non-NHS sexual health clinics do not always offer the full range of services which are available at NHS sexual health clinics.)

Some sexual health clinics offer men-only and women-only sessions and some offer sessions for gay and bisexual men and women. (Ring the London Lesbian and Gay Switchboard or the National AIDS Helpline.)

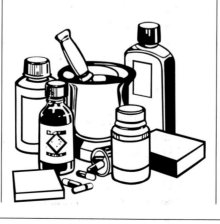

What happens at the clinic?
When you arrive, the receptionist will ask you to complete a registration form. You may then be given a card with a personal identification number to retain your anonymity.

You will be seen by a nurse, health adviser or doctor, who will ask you some questions about your general and sexual health. These include questions about your sexual activities and whether they were with a man, a woman or both. You may find these questions embarrassing but it is important that you answer them honestly to help staff find out which tests you need.

What tests are available?
Once you have discussed your worries, the doctor decides what type of examination and tests you need.

A full sexual health check includes:
- An examination of your genitals and sometimes the lower part of your body, your mouth and skin.
- Taking a few swabs. A swab is a type of cotton bud used to pick up samples of any discharge or secretions from your genital region.
- A urine sample.
- A blood test for syphilis (offered to all patients).

You may also be offered:
- An HIV test. This will only be done if you specifically agree to it.
- A cervical smear test (if you are a woman).
- Blood tests for hepatitis B and C.

You may get some of your test results straight away. But other results take longer, and you must phone or call in to collect them. If your results show that you have an infection, you will be given treatment immediately.

If you are given antibiotics to take away, it is important that you finish the course – even if the symptoms go away before the tablets are finished. Do not share your treatment with partners or friends.

The clinic may advise you to contact any recent partners and ask them to attend for a check-up. If this is difficult for you, help is at hand.

© Health Education Authority
January, 1998

ADDITIONAL RESOURCES

You might like to contact the following organisations for further information. Due to the increasing cost of postage, many organisations cannot respond to enquiries unless they receive a stamped, addressed envelope.

Aids Care, Education and Training (ACET)
PO Box 3693
27a Carlton Drive
Putney
London, SW15 2BQ
Tel: 0181 780 0400
In communities around the world ACET provides unconditional care for those with HIV/AIDS, practical education and training about HIV and its prevention.

AIDS Education and Research Trust (AVERT)
4 Brighton Road
Horsham
West Sussex, RH13 5BA
Tel: 01403 210202
AVERT aims to prevent people becoming infected with HIV, to improve the quality of life for those already infected and to work with others to develop a cure. Publishes a wide range of educational booklets. Ask for their Resources Catalogue.

AIDS Reference Manual
NAM Publications
16a Clapham Common Southside
London, SW4 7AB
Tel: 0171 627 3200
The *AIDS Reference Manual* is available as a component part of the National AIDS Manual or as an independent publication.

Brook Advisory Centres
165 Gray's Inn Road
London, WC1X 8UD
Tel: 0171 713 9000
Brook is a professional non-profit making organisation for young people up to the age of 25. It exists to enable all young people to make informed choices about their personal and sexual relationships.

CAB International
Wallingford
Oxon, OX10 8DE
Tel: 01491 832 111
Publishes *AIDS Newsletter* and *Current AIDS Literature*. They also produce a CD ROM, *CAB Health*, which is a compilation of current journal articles, book extracts, conference reports and papers.

ChildLine
2nd Floor Royal Mail Building
Studd Street
London, N1 0QW
Tel: 0171 239 1000 (admin)
Fax: 0171 239 1001
ChildLine is free, national helpline for children and young people in trouble or danger. Provides confidential phone counselling service for any child with any problem 24 hours a day. Produces publications. Children or young people can phone or write free of charge about problems of any kind to: ChildLine, Freepost 1111, London N1 0BR, Tel: Freephone 0800 1111

Health Education Authority – HQ
Trevelyan House
30 Great Peter Street
London, SW1P 2HW
Tel: 0171 222 5300
Develops and implements health campaigns both nationally and internationally, offers a range of services to public and private sectors, and advises the government on health education matters. Publishes a wide range of educational booklets.

National AIDS Helpline
Freephone: 0800 567 123
A 24-hour helpline for anyone concerned about HIV and AIDS or any other sexual health matter. Distribute a free range of information sheets.

National AIDS Trust
New City Cloisters
18/196 Old Street
London, EC1V 9FR
Tel: 0171 814 6767
The National AIDS Trust aims to promote a wider understanding of HIV and AIDS, develop and support efforts to prevent the spread of HIV, and improve the quality of life of people affected by HIV and AIDS.

National Children's Bureau
8 Wakely Street
London, EC1V 7QE
Tel: 0171 843 6000
Provides information on children's needs in the family, school and society. They publish a series of factsheets called Highlights including *HIV and children* (Highlight No. 129).

NCH Action for Children
85 Highbury Park
London, N5 1UD
Tel: 0171 226 2033
NCH Action for Children is the largest child care charity in Britain, offering a wide range of service. Publishes a wide range of educational booklets.

Scottish AIDS Monitor
26 Anderson Place
Edinburgh, EH6 5NP
Tel: 0131 555 4850
Provides a wide range of services throughout Scotland.

Sex Education Forum
National Children's Bureau
8 Wakely Street
London, EC1V 7QE
Tel: 0171 843 6054
Produces publications including a set of factsheets and a termly newsletter called *Sex Education Matters.*

Terrence Higgins Trust
52-54 Gray's Inn Road
London, WC1X 8JU
Tel: 0171 831 0330
Runs a phone helpline. Provides training and practical support for people with AIDS and their family and friends. Publishes a wide range of educational booklets.

INDEX

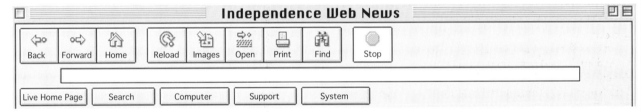

The Internet has been likened to shopping in a supermarket without aisles. The press of a button on a Web browser can bring up thousands of sites but working your way through them to find what you want can involve long and frustrating on-line searches. And unfortunately many sites contain inaccurate, misleading or heavily biased information. Our researchers have therefore undertaken an extensive analysis to bring you a selection of quality Web site addresses. If our readers feel that this new innovation in the series is useful, we plan to provide a more extensive Web site section in each new book in the *Issues* series.

* * * * *

AIDS Education and Research Trust (AVERT)
www.avert.org
This site focuses on information about education to prevent infection with HIV, information for HIV positive people and the latest news and statistics.

AIDS Treatment Project (ATP)
www.unaids.org/highband/index.html
A large range of factsheets, statistics, press releases and other relevant information.

National AIDS Trust (NAT)
www.nat.org.uk/nat
The NAT web site contains news and information, on-line publications, contact details, project details, an events diary and links to other web sites.

New York On-line Access to Health
(NOAH)www.noah.cuny.edu/aids/aids.html
Provides comprehensive information on a wide variety of HIV/AIDS related issues.

Terrence Higgins Trust
http://www.tht.org.uk/pubs
An impressive range of on-line publications covers most aspects of HIV/AIDS.

The Naked Truth
www.unspeakable.com
The Naked Truth is a public health outreach project provided as an educational service by Pfizer Inc. This site describes the main STDs, has factsheets, a quiz and plenty of other useful information.

UK HIV/AIDS Web Site Directory
www.posnet.co.uk/public/uksites.htm
An impressive listing of major HIV/AIDS web sites.

World Health Organisation (WHO)
www.who.ch/programmes/emc/bsefacts.htm
Working together with national AIDS programmes throughout the world, the United Nations Joint Programme on HIV/AIDS and the World Health Organisation have surveyed the global epidemic of HIV/AIDS. This major new report, the fruit of this surveillance and analysis, gives much more detail than has been previously published about the global epidemic, the evolving picture in different regions, and the situation in individual countries at the end of 1997. See also: www.who.ch/inf-fs/en/index.html

* * * * * *

ACKNOWLEDGEMENTS

The publisher is grateful for permission to reproduce the following material.

While every care has been taken to trace and acknowledge copyright, the publisher tenders its apology for any accidental infringement or where copyright has proved untraceable. The publisher would be pleased to come to a suitable arrangement in any such case with the rightful owner.

Chapter One: HIV and AIDS

Understanding HIV and AIDS, © Terrence Higgins Trust, April 1998, *UK HIV and AIDS update*, © National AIDS Trust, *Statistics*, © National AIDS Trust, *Sexual diseases epidemic getting worse as Aids claims 10,000*, © The Independent, June 1997, *New cases of HIV in 1997*, © UNAIDS/World Health Organization (WHO), *Aids 2000*, © Aids 2000, *Young people at risk*, © UNAIDS, *Orphaned children*, © UNAIDS/World Health Organization (WHO), *Tragedy on an epic scale*, © The Guardian, December 1997, *AIDS statistics*, © UNAIDS, *Over 27 million do not know they are infected*, © UNAIDS, January, 1998, *HIV and Aids update*, © AIDS Care, Education and Training (ACET), 1998, *World turned upside down*, © The Guardian, June 1997, *Cases of HIV/Aids*, © UNAIDS, *The history of AIDS*, © AIDS Reference Manual 1997, *What does HIV do?*, © AIDS Care, Education and Training (ACET), *Pregnant women let down by HIV tests*, © The Independent, January 1998, *Global summary of the HIV/AIDS epidemic*, © UNAIDS/World Health Organization (WHO), *Aids: why shouldn't mothers be told the truth?*, © The Independent, December 1997, *Life imprisonment for 'intentional' transmission*, © Vanguard AIDS Newsletter, April 1998, *Testing issues*, © Terrence Higgins Trust, January 1998, *Aids in US is spreading faster among women than men*, © The Independent, September 1997, *Aids: and now for the bad news*, © The Guardian, May, 1997, *Complementary therapies*, © The CrusAID & STAR Information Exchange, 1997.

Chapter Two: Sexually Transmitted Diseases

Sexually transmitted diseases, © World Health Organization, 1998, *Sexually transmitted diseases and young people*, © World Health Organization, 1998, *Distribution of STDs by age group and sex*, © Communicable Diseases Report, February 1998, *Warts and all*, © Nursing Times, January 1998, *Screening for sexually transmitted disease*, © The Independent, May 1998, *Young people's sexual attitudes and behaviour*, © Sex Education Forum/ National Children's Bureau, Autumn 1997, *Sexually transmitted infections*, © Health Education Authority, January 1998.

Photographs and illustrations:

Page 1: Andrew Smith, pages 12, 16, 22, 29, 33, 37, 39: The Attic Publishing Co.

Thank you

Darin Jewell for assisting in the editorial research for this publication.

Craig Donnellan
Cambridge
September, 1998